AMYNTAS

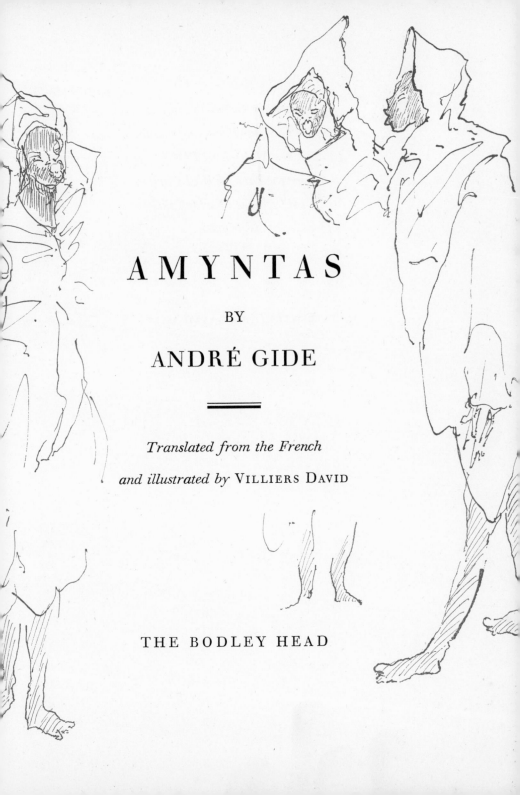

AMYNTAS

BY

ANDRÉ GIDE

====

Translated from the French

and illustrated by VILLIERS DAVID

THE BODLEY HEAD

Printed in Great Britain at
The Curwen Press and bound
by Mansell in 1958
under the care of Will Carter,
1500 copies of which this
is number
1363

To M.A.G.

TRANSLATOR'S NOTE

A friend's warm gratitude is due to
H.E. Hussein Ali Garagozlou for his invaluable
assistance throughout the preparation
of this translation

CONTENTS

'There were not very many to notice that I had never written anything more perfect than Amyntas . . . To whom could the secret value of the book speak? Only to a few rare souls; the others were disappointed.'

Journal, 14th Nov. 1910

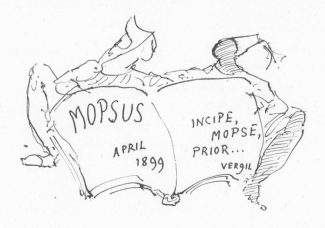

I

El Kantara

. . . The rock-wall, which has since morning flanked us, opens at last. Here is the gateway; we are through.

It is evening; we had been walking in shadow; the fullness of the dying day revives. – Lovely, desirable land, oh, for such ecstasy, such repose, you now spread yourself out beneath this warm and golden light.

We stop; wait; stare.

A different world appears; strange, immobile, impassive, drained of colour. – Joyous? no; sad? no: serene.

We approach; as if through tepid, clouded water, through the palm shadows, timidly and step by step, we advance . . . Flute-notes; a white gesture; gently whispering water; a child's laughter at the water's side – then nothing; not a care now, not a thought. It is not even repose, for here there is never a stir. The air is soft. – What did I desire until today? Over what did I distress myself?

1

II

Evening comes; the flocks return. What one had thought to be stillness was really numbness and torpor; the wondering oasis for an instant quivers and aspires to life; an infinitely light breath stirs the palms; blue smoke rises from each earthen house and etherializes the village which, once the flocks returned, prepares for sleep and sinks into a night as soft as death.

III

Let life, uninterrupted, pursue its course. The old man dies without a sound and the child grows up without a quiver. The village endures unchanged, for, where none aspires to betterment, the novelty of any effort is unknown.

Village of narrow streets; here, there is no luxury to oblige poverty to recognize itself. All things rest and smile amidst their frugal felicity. Simple labours in the fields, the golden age! Then, on the door-steps at dusk, to while away with songs and stories the leisure of the slow evening . . .

IV

There, between the heavy, styleless pillars of the dim room some women are dancing, tall women, more weird than beautiful, and extravagantly adorned. They move slowly. The voluptuousness which they dispense is grave and strong and secret, like death. Near the café on a courtyard shared in common, full of the moon's light or the night's, each one keeps her door half-open. Their beds are low. You step into them as into a tomb. – Dreamily some Arabs watch the

2

swaying dance, led by music, ceaseless as the sound of running water. The café-keeper brings the coffee in a tiny cup, from which you would think you were draining oblivion.

V

Of all the Moorish cafés I have chosen the darkest, the most secluded. What attracts me? Nothing; shadows; a supple, shifting figure; a song; — and not to be seen from outside; the sense of secrecy.

I enter noiselessly; I sit down quickly, and, to disturb no one, pretend to read; I will wait and see . . .

But no; nothing. — An old Arab sleeps in a corner; another sings in a low voice; under a seat a dog gnaws a bone; and the child-keeper of the café, by the hearth, stirs the ashes for a few embers, on which to heat my brackish coffee. The time that flows here has no hours; but so perfect is the inactivity of all, that here to be bored becomes impossible.

VI

What have I wanted until today? For what was I toiling? Oh, now I recognize the garden, outside time, where time rests. Cloistered realm, serene, Arcadia! . . . I have found the land of repose.

Here the carefree gesture plucks, without pursuing, the moment; unwearyingly minute repeats minute; hour repeats hour; and today echoes yesterday.

Bleating of the flocks in the evening; drifting notes of the reed-pipes beneath the palms; unending cooing of the doves. — O nature without aim, without sorrow and never changing,

3

– thus you smiled on the gentlest of poets; thus, to my pious eyes, you will smile . . .

This evening I saw the trapped water spread to quench the thirsty plants and refresh the garden. A black child, wading with bare feet in the canal, controlled as he wished the thriftily planned irrigation. He opened and closed tiny sluices set in the clay. One allotted to each tree, they poured out water round the tree-trunks.

In the cracked hollows I saw this water rise, thick with earth, warm and yellowed by a ray of the sun. Then, at last, the water, spilling over and pouring rivulets in all directions, flooded a whole field of barley . . .

Claudite jam rivos, pueri; sat prata biberunt.

VII

Too fierce, the sun has almost dried the river. But here, beneath its vault of foliage, the oued flows and deepens; further on, it rises to the sun again to languish on a bank of sand.

. . . Ah! ah! to dip one's hands in this blond water! to drink! to bathe one's naked feet! plunge into it altogether . . . ah! glowing content! In the shade, there, this stream is cool as the night. A roving sunbeam pierces the meshes of the foliage, stabs the shade, quivers and, like an arrow, leaps; it cleaves and penetrates the water's depths, makes it laugh and, right at the bottom but without insistence, touches lightly a little sand which shifts . . . Oh! to swim!

I want to stretch myself naked on the bank; the sand is hot, yielding, light. – Oh! the sun scorches, penetrates me; I burst,

4

I melt, evaporate, etherialize in the azure air. Oh! delicious burns! – Oh! oh! may so much light, absorbed, give fresh nourishment to my fever, more richness to my fervour and more fire to my kiss!

VIII

Taking off our shoes, which were filling with sand, we were able with an immense effort to climb the dune we had reached and which shut out the horizon.

Shifting dune; to reach it, all the rawness of this land, the waterless ravines, the thorns without flowers were brought home to us. The sand, driven towards us by the wind, blinded us. When we wanted to climb the dune, it sank and yielded beneath our steps; the foot was swallowed by it; it seemed as if we did not move, or that the whole dune withdrew. And, though it was not high, it took us a long time to climb it.

Beyond the dune the country was even more immense, but otherwise exactly similar. Exhausted, we sat down in a strip of shade, sheltered a little from the wind. At the very top of the dune the wind, raising and driving back the sand, constantly remodelled the crest.

Around us, over us, over everything, one could hear the sand falling, as imperceptibly, as lightly as silence. We were soon covered . . . We set off again.

IX

The road of shadow and half-light winds between the enclosed gardens.

Walls of clay! I will sing your praise, for the gardens' green profusion overflows you; low walls! the branch of the

5

apricot-tree cares nothing for you; it passes over you, springs forward, floats across my path. Earthen walls! above you, the leaning palm-trees sway; the palm-leaves shade my path. From garden to garden, across my path, unafraid of you, crumbling walls, the fluttering ring-doves visit one another. – Through a breach a vine-shoot slips, straightens itself and on to the palm's trunk leaps; coils about it, encompasses it, stifles it, gains an apricot-tree, settles on it; hesitates, falls back, divides itself; spreads out its thickening stems. Oh, in what burning month, climbing that tree, will some slim child stretch out towards my hand, to quench my thirst, a plucked and heavy cluster?

. . . Walls of clay, without wearying, hoping you may at last yield, I follow you.

A seguia runs by the clay wall; it flows beside the path. The wall fills the path with shade. In the garden I hear a hint of laughter and the hum of charming remarks . . . O beautiful garden!

All at once the water escapes; piercing the wall, it enters; it advances into the garden; on its way a sunbeam stabs it; – the garden is full of sun.

Earthen walls! hateful walls! my ceaseless desire besieges you; be sure, I will succeed at last in entering.

X

Sunk in the earth-wall a little wooden door is concealed.

We shall arrive in front of that little low door, to which a child will have the key; we shall stoop; we shall make ourselves small to enter. 'Oh!' we shall say, – 'oh! this is a peaceful place. Oh! we did not know we could rest so well and

6

*find so calm a spot on this earth . . . Bring us flutes and milk
– we shall stretch ourselves on mats; a little palm-wine and
some dates; we shall stay here until evening.' – A light wind
flees through the palms; the shadows hesitate; the sun laughs;
beneath the giant apricot-trees the ditches of yellowish water
turn to blue; the fig-trees creep along the ground; but what
especially enchants us is the grace of the oleanders.*

*Do not let us move again; let time close in like a wave, like
a wave into which a pebble has been thrown; the disturbance
we caused by entering fades away like the wave's ripple: let
us leave the smooth surface of time to close over this world
again.*

XI

*We had risen very early that morning, so that before the
heat we had been able to cover a great distance. – Oh! how
interminably the oasis stretches on! For how long shall we
walk, caught thus between the walls of the gardens? – I know
that near the limit of the oasis all these walls come to an end,
that the path hesitates amongst the freed trunks of the palms.
– Little by little the palms thin out; one would think they were
lagging or were discouraged. – Their shafts, less entwined,
sway more disconsolately . . . Still a few remain. Between
them the country opens out. – The oasis is at an end.
Nothing more separates our eye from the bare horizon. –*

Let us stop! The great desert unfurls here. – Let us stop. –

*Look! on the tawny, motionless sea float, like islands, the
motionless oases.*

*Behind us a flank of fiery rock, at which the northern gales
halt; at times a cloud passes, a flake of white; it hesitates, disintegrates and, dishevelled, is absorbed into the azure.*

7

Farther away, above the hot wall, behind us, is the mountain around which the azure streams.

Ahead of us, nothing; — the delicately-hued emptiness of the desert.

XII

Mopsus to Menalchus

If Damon laments Daphnis still, if Gallus Lycoris — let them come; I shall guide their footsteps to oblivion. — Here no nourishment for their grief; a great calm over their thought. — Here, more voluptuous and more useless is it to live and less difficult to die.

LEAVES BY THE
WAYSIDE
MARCH–APRIL
1896

Our arrival in Tunis in the autumn, three years ago, was marvellous. Though it had already been much spoilt by the broad avenues which cross it, it was still a fine, classical city, uniform and harmonious, and its white-washed houses seemed to light up at night, intimately, like alabaster lamps.

As soon as you left the French port, you never saw another tree; you had to look for shade in the souks, those large markets, vaulted or covered with awnings or planks; only a reflected light penetrated them, filling them with an atmosphere all their own; these souks were like a second town, underground, within the town, – and about as large as a third of Tunis. – From the height of the terrace where P.L. used to go and paint, you saw as far as the sea only a descending stairway of white terraces slashed by courtyards, like pits, in which the women whiled away the tedium of their days. In the evening all the whites became mauve and the sky the colour of a tea-rose; in the morning the whites became pink against a faintly violet sky. – But after the winter rains the walls clothe themselves in vegetation; they

9

are covered in green mosses, and the edges of the terraces look like those of a flower-basket.

I missed the white, grave, classical Tunis of the autumn, which reminded me, as I wandered through its orderly streets at night, of Helen in the Second Part of Faust, or of Psyche, 'the agate lamp in her hand', wandering in an avenue of sepulchres.

Trees are being planted along the wide streets and in the squares. Tunis will be more charming because of them, yet nothing could disfigure it so much. Two years ago, Rue Marr and the Place des Moutons were still such that one did not know where one had been set down, and the farthest Orient, the most secret Africa could, I believe, have offered no more startling impression of the weird. A different style of life, which everything visible embodies, very full, ancient, classical, long-established; no compromise yet between the civilizations of the East and ours, which appears especially ugly when it wants to patch and repair. – Sheets of iron or of zinc are replacing little by little the reed mattings for the roofing of the souks, and street-lamps scatter a fitful light over walls, where of old, night shed an even brightness, – over that large Place des Moutons, without pavements, silent, marvellous, where, two years ago, during the mild nights of the full moon, beside their herds of camels, Arabs came to sleep.

– Pavements have been laid in the souks. Down one of the finest passages, the bases of the little columns which support the vault have been hidden in the ground. Small, twisted pillars, in green and red, with massive, wrought capitals. The vault is white-washed but receives hardly any light. Even on the brightest days these souks are always half plunged in darkness.

10

The entrance to the souks is marvellous; I am not speaking of the portal of the mosque, but of that other, narrow, secluded entrance – sheltered by a leaning jujube-tree which provides a fore-court of shadow for the dark little passage, which takes a sharp turn and is at once lost to sight. But the jujube-tree, covered with leaves in autumn, is still bare in the spring. – It is the starting point of the saddlers' souk; the passage takes a turn, then continues interminably.

In the souk of perfumes, Sadouk-Anoun for ever sits like a cobbler in his shop, no larger than a niche, its floor at elbow-height, crowded with phials; but the perfumes he sells now are adulterated. On my return to Paris I gave P.V. the two last genuine flasks, which I saw Sadouk-Anoun himself fill from a little tube with the essence of apples and, drop by drop, with precious amber. Since, today, they are half filled with a commoner product, he does not wrap them round so scrupulously with virgin wax and white thread, and does not charge me so much. Three years ago his meticulousness amused us; it seemed to add value to his goods. With each additional wrapping the perfume acquired more rarity. At last we would stop him; we could never have afforded the price.

– I have also searched in vain for that dark café, to which came only the tall negroes of the Sudan. Some had had a toe cut off as a sign of slavery. Most of them wore, tucked under their turban, a little sprig of white flowers, of sweet-smelling jasmine; this sprig falls across the cheek like a romantic curl, and gives their faces an expression of voluptuous languor. They so much love the scent of flowers that sometimes, not smelling them strongly enough to their liking in this way, they thrust the crumpled petals into their nostrils. – In this café one of them used to sing, another to

11

tell stories; and pigeons fluttered and settled on their shoulders.

Tunis, 7th March

Little children see this, laugh, and repeat to one another the lewd mimicries of Caracous. – A difficult exercise for the mind: that it should have to reform itself until it finds all this quite natural . . . What does the audience of children, of children only and, for the most part, of tiny ones think of it?

The French do not go there; they do not know where these places are; for these are small inconspicuous shops; one creeps in through a low door. The French regularly go to the neighbouring showmen, who make a great display and attract tourists only; the Arabs know what to think of all that and that it does not amount to much, the cardboard horse which dances, the camel of wood and cloth, which dances also and indeed very funnily, but in the manner altogether of a travelling-show. But nearby, there is a shop for traditional Caracous, classical, simple, nothing could be simpler, with an admirable stage-convention by which Caracous hides himself, at the centre of the stage, between two policemen who look for him, merely because he has lowered his head and can no longer see them; – and the children accept this, understand and laugh.

Caracous. – A small, long room, during the day a shop and stall, which is dismantled at night; a little stage is set up at the back with a transparent canvas curtain for the shadows. At right angles to the stage, two benches against the walls. These are the privileged seats. The middle of the room fills with very young children, who sit on the ground

12

and jostle one another. Quantities of dried, salted melon-seeds are eaten, a delicacy so enticing that my pocket, filled every morning for twopence, is empty every night. It is true I give some of them to the children.

An amusing feature here are the wall-niches, sorts of very uncomfortable berths, like nests of sea-swallows, into which one can climb only by pulling oneself up with one's arms, and from which one does not descend – but drops down, – which are hired out only for the whole evening to the young aficionados. I came back here many an evening; there was almost always the same audience, in the same seats, listening to the same plays and laughing at the same places – like myself.

Caracous. – Another shop; some Sudanese. Where there are Sudanese, the Arabs do not willingly go. So here one sees only negroes. But this evening I find my friend R. here also.

The play has not begun. (The intervals are always longer than the play; this particular play does not last a quarter of an hour.) One negro clacks castanets, another raps on an oblong drum, and the third, a giant, rocks and shakes himself in front of R.; crouched almost at our feet, he sings, improvising a monotonous lament, in which he recounts, as far as I can understand him, that he is very poor, that R. is very rich and that negroes are always in need of money. And as he looks a bit fierce and as the Arabs maintain that one cannot trust for very long a camel, a negro, or the desert, we quickly become very charitable.

Caracous. – Another shop. Here the play is merely an excuse for assignations. Always the same habitués, night after night, under the benevolent eye of the patron. A strangely beautiful child plays the bagpipe; everyone gathers round him; they are his admirers. One of them plays on that curious urn-shaped drum, the head of which is made out of a donkey's skin. He, the bagpipe-player, is the success of the café, seems to smile at everyone and to favour no one. Some recite verses to him and sing them; he replies to them, draws near, but I think everything stops short at a few flatteries exchanged in front of everyone; this shop is not a low den, but rather a court of love. Sometimes one of them gets up and dances, sometimes two; then the dance becomes a rather free mimicry.

The play, elsewhere just as here, is almost always obscene. I would like to know the history of Caracous. His origin must be very ancient. I was told he came from Constantinople and that everywhere else but in Constantinople and Tunis the police would have forbidden his presentation on the stage; he is only to be seen during Ramadan. The people fast for forty days from sunrise to nightfall; a total fast; neither food, nor drink, nor tobacco, nor scents, nor women. All the senses, chastised during the day, take their revenge

14

at night, and everyone amuses himself as best he can. There are also, of course, very religious Arabs, who, after a very frugal meal, spend each night of Ramadan in meditation and prayer; just as there are others who continue to amuse themselves even during the day; but that is not common except in the big towns which the Roumis have corrupted. The Arabs are usually, and almost all of them, most scrupulously orthodox.

My last night, I wanted to look once again, before taking flight, at all the rarest and most exotic things that Tunis had shown me. I shall recall that military band I followed for a long time on its way back to its barracks – its music very sonorous, true, beautiful and victorious – whilst on the seafront and along the French boulevards, here and there out of the foliage of the pepper-trees Bengal lights fashioned a faint pink filigree.

Few of the Arabs turned their heads as the band passed; the shrill music in their own cafés continued.

Many of them recall, I think, the day when in triumph that band entered for the first time their conquered city. I asked myself uneasily whether in their thoughts there still remained nothing but hate for the French.

I looked for pleasure along the Rue Marr; but I thought regretfully of the Halfaouïne. I found quite a large, fine, Moorish café, but they hardly tolerated me there. The French never go to it. The liveliness of the Halfaouïne attracts them; the other quarters of the town are silent. An old negro began dancing grotesquely to the sound of a bagpipe and the beating of a drum.

I returned to the Halfaouïne along the dark boulevards. Not many people; nothing in particular. Towards the end of the evening, I found R. in the same Caracous shop to

15

which I had taken him the first day. He understands too the interest there is in returning regularly to the same places to study not many but a few faces well, and not just to watch them pass before one's eyes. The Arabs grow accustomed to one, one seems less strange to them and they resume their ordinary behaviour, which had at first been ruffled.

El Kantara

We arrived here at the end of the day – a day of splendour. Athman had arrived in the morning, had slept a little in the afternoon, but had been waiting at the station an hour for us. And that hour had seemed long to him. – 'And yet,' he told me, 'I thought: now there is no more than an hour; before, there was a whole year . . .'

Three burnouses; a white silk gandourah lined with blue silk and trimmed with pink; a jacket of pastel-blue cloth; the enormous turban of brown cording, clasping the fine white fabric which hangs down, brushes the cheek, and billows beneath the chin. This head-dress transforms him; last year, aged sixteen, he still wore the simple chéchia for children; at seventeen he must have the elaborate turban for men. Athman has spent everything he possesses on his 'costume'; he has dressed himself up for the reunion. But for his welcome, I would hardly have recognized him.

Evening fell slowly; we crossed the gorge and the fabulous East calmly appeared before us peacefully arrayed in gold. We went down under the palm-trees and left Athman to wait in the road for the carriage which was to follow us. I recognized all the sounds – of the running water, of the birds. Everything was as it had been before, calm; our arrival altered nothing.

16

In our carriage we skirted the oasis for quite a long way. On our way back the sun was setting; we pulled up in front of a Moorish café; the hour of Ramadan was past. In the courtyard, near us, some rutting camels were fighting. A keeper was shouting at them. The flocks of goats returned.

A thin vapour, a blue smoke rose from all the grey earthen houses and soon enveloped the whole oasis and seemed to veil it in distance. The sky in the west was of a most pure blue, so transparent that it seemed still suffused with light. The silence became wonderful; one could not conceive even of a song there. I felt that I loved this land perhaps more than any other . . .

Biskra

Yesterday we were in the gardens: we followed the paths which first led us to N'Msid, then to Bab el Derb. We reached the old fort and returned through Sidi Barkat. It was a long walk and it tired M. – Athman was with us and R.; Larbi accompanied us. We had coffee at the entrance to N'Msid, in front of the bed of the Oued, Laliah, and the peaks of the Aurès.

I do not like this landscape so much as the vague expanse of the desert on the other side. Larbi, a charming cheat, played dominoes with us. I am waiting for Jammes with delicious impatience. Here the country speaks a different language, but one I understand now.

My room last year was on the ground-floor of the hotel; when my window was open, only the height of the ledge separated me from the outside; it could be cleared in a jump. Sadeck, Athman's big brother, and several others from old Biskra used to come and rest in my room during Ramadan before returning to their village. I had dates,

17

cakes, syrups and jams. It was night-time; Sadeck played the flute and we would readily remain silent for a long time.

At night I closed only the shutters. All the sounds from outside came in. Every morning they woke me before dawn and I went to the edge of the desert to watch the sunrise. This was the moment when Lassif's flock passed by, made up of the goats of the poor; as they had no garden of their own, they entrusted him with their goats every morning; Lassif took them to graze in the desert. He went from door to door knocking before dawn; the door opened and let out a few goats for him. By the time he left the village he had more than sixty.

He went very far off with them, towards the Hot Springs where there are chokeweeds and euphorbiaceae. He had a huge billy-goat on which he sometimes rode when the way was tiring, or to distract him, for he could not play the flute. When he had left one morning without passing my window, I went to meet him in the desert.

I immensely love the desert. The first year, I feared it a little because of its wind and sand, then, as I had no objective, I never knew when to stop and I tired myself very quickly. I preferred the shady paths beneath the palm-trees, the gardens of Ouardi, the villages. But last year I took tremendous walks. I had no other object than to be out of sight of the oasis. I walked; I walked until I felt myself immensely alone in the plain. Then I began to look around me. The sands had a dappled bloom of shadows on the slopes of their hillocks; there were marvellous rustlings on every breeze; because of the huge silence, the lightest sound reached one's ears. Sometimes in the direction of the great dune an eagle soared. This monotonous expanse appeared to me day by day to have a more lovely-seeming diversity.

18

I knew the keepers of the nomad flocks; I sought them out; I talked with them; some of them played the flute exquisitely. Sometimes I sat beside them for a long time, doing nothing; I always took a book with me, but hardly ever opened it. Often it was night before I came home. — But Athman, whom I told of these outings, said they were imprudent, and that roving Arabs keep watch on the approaches to the oases and plunder strangers, whom they know cannot defend themselves; they would have been following their calling by attacking me. From that day he wanted to accompany me; but as he did not like walking, my outings grew shorter, then came to an end.

Athman reads like Bouvard and writes like Pecuchet. He teaches himself with all his might and copies out anything and everything. He prefers *La joie de Maguelonne* by Herold, to *La tentative amoureuse*; he finds my *Tentative* badly written. 'You use the word *"grass"* too often,' he tells me.

I give him the *Thousand and One Nights*. One evening he takes the book to Bordj Boulakras, where he sleeps, to read it with his friend, Bachaga. The next day he does not arrive until ten o'clock, still heavy with sleep; he and his friend read the story of Aladdin until two in the morning, he tells me; and adds: 'Oh! we spent a very pleasant nocturnal night!' — Nocturnal, means for him, staying up late.

At the end of the oasis, among the deserted ruins of the old fort, near which we are passing on this night of full moon, some Arabs, clothed in white and stretched out on the ground, talk in undertones and one of them whispers on

19

the flute. 'They are going to spend a nocturnal night', Athman says to me, 'telling each other stories.' – In the summer one would not dare lie down like this; scorpions and horned vipers, which hide in the sand during the day, come out and prowl at night-fall. – Farther on, we get out of our carriage; there are no more palm-trees; the night seems to enlarge the desert, brimming over with blue light. Even Jammes is silent. And suddenly Athman is seized with lyrical exuberance, casts off his burnous, tucks in his gandourah and turns a cartwheel in the moonlight.

Athman has found I don't know what 'Lives of Famous Men' – and now, when he mentions camels, quotes Buffon and Cuvier; no longer speaks of friendship without a reference to Henri IV and Sully, of courage without citing Bayard, and of the Great Bear without naming Galileo.

He writes to Degas and sends him a stick made out of a palm-stalk; he says to him: 'What pleases me is that you don't like the Jews, and that you read *La Libre Parole*, and that, like myself, you consider that Poussin is a great French painter.'

Jammes amuses himself by making him read the following verses improvised while waiting for the carriage which is to take us to Droh:

To my friend Athman

> Athman, my dear friend,
> Trees with almonds on their twigs,
> Blackcurrants and trees with figs,
> Were created to be sat
> Under when one's tired and flat.

Down one lies,
Not stirring, and shuts one's eyes
Happily, lazily.
Under the garden lurks a spring,
And its water-crystals sing
Like an Arab girl.

To be so idle is so nice,
And sleepily to shut one's eyes
As if one were in bed.
It is so very nice, Athman,
That wholly idle state,
That one thinks one's dead.

Since Jammes is here, Athman spends day and night writing verses. At times he finds some pretty phrases:

Beneath the palms, there are no concerts . . .

or again:

. . . He who has known
Love has drunk deeply bitter waters
And Time interests him no more.

But I often fear that he finds them only by chance. Besides, he is only seventeen.

He continues to read the *Thousand and One Nights* assiduously; knows the story of Aladdin by heart, and now signs his letters:

'ATHMAN OR THE WONDERFUL LAMP'

Jammes has given me his stick. It is made of ironwood and comes from the West Indies; it amuses the native children because the handle is the head of a greyhound; it is as polished as jade, and yet so crude that it might have been carved with a knife. I have never seen anything so strange. Along the shaft there are verses in capital letters, as follows:

'A squirrel had a
Rose in his mouth, a donkey
Thought him mad.'

And this, which he put at the top of his letters:

'A bee slumbers
Amongst the briars of my heart.'

Touggourt, 7th April

An Arab well-sinker is being given a decoration today.

Before the advent of drilling companies and artesian wells, the Arabs had well-sinkers. Sometimes it is necessary to bore to a depth of 70 or 80 metres to find spring-water. Men are employed to go down the shaft.

They are trained young for this painful profession, but many die by it. Three strata of soil and two of water – the first stagnant, the second just seeping up, have to be pierced, before the last level of spring water is finally reached. The water wells up then, at times wonderfully clear and abundant, but almost always laden with sodium and magnesium. The effort these well-sinking divers must make to work under water is incredible; this particular man was, they said, one of the bravest. A well or passage has to be constructed through the middle of the water, which the water itself will not penetrate and in which work and further boring can be done, two borings in fact, through these two liquid strata, to lay a pipe so that the fresh water can gush through the stagnant water without being contaminated.

23

That same day, in one of those rectangular wells, made of palm-trunks, we saw a man, slung on a rope, go down – to a depth of 60 metres – to repair some damage.

And so, the Arab well-sinker was given a decoration; in the evening, he went mad.

The bed of the stagnant water, at Touggourt, is almost level with the ground. Here there are no longer the fine flowing waters of Chetna or the rippling canals of Biskra, only evil-smelling ditches full of foul grass. However, a river also flows across the oasis, which is carefully portioned for the palm-trees. At the bottom, amongst the weeds, grass-snakes glide.

Sands ring the oasis; yesterday a frightening storm blew them on high. The horizon seemed to fold over us like a blanket you pull up; we could see nothing; we could scarcely breathe.

Not far from the town there is a wretched cemetery, which the sand is slowly engulfing. One can still make out a few tombs.

In the desert the idea of death pursues you; but, wonderful fact, it is not a sad idea here. At Biskra, behind the old fort, at the very centre of the oasis, the rains have ploughed up the ancient cemetery and, as the dead are buried un-coffined in the ground, the loose bones in certain places are as abundant as pebbles.

The sand-storm raged till the evening; at sunset we climbed the minaret. The palm-trees were lustreless and the town was panting beneath an ash-coloured sky.

A tremendous wind blew out of the East, like a prophetic blast of divine malediction that prophets might have presaged. And in the midst of this desolation we saw a caravan *setting out.*

The Ouled dance better here than at Biskra and are more beautiful; indeed it is here alone that I have seen them dance well. We came back without boredom to this grave and languid dance, almost entirely performed with the arms and the wrists, and very proper, – and we were dazed, almost exhausted, by that dogged, rapid, quivering, provocative music, which rouses one to ecstasy, which does not stop when one takes leave of it and which haunts me still some evenings, like the desert itself.

I would like to have spent tonight in the square, where the caravans were camping. There were watch-fires of brushwood; around them Arabs were talking in low voices; some were singing; they sang throughout the night.

Athman tells me the story of Uriah's wife.

According to Arab tradition, it was while pursuing a golden dove from hall to hall in his palace that David, whom he calls Daoud, finally reached that upper terrace from which he could see Bathsheba.

Athman relates: '. . . the Jew told him that Moses was right and that God would gather first the Jew, and then the Arabs, and perhaps even the Christians. The Christian told him that Christ was right, and that God would take unto himself the Christians, but the Arabs as well and even the Jews. The Arab told him that Mohammed was right, and that God would receive in his paradise the Arabs, but that he would shut the door on the unconverted Jews and on Christians. And when he had heard all three, he hastened to become a Mussulman.'

The Christians have the right of seniority over the Arabs. They say, or at any rate like to say to me, that if before dying a Christian utters the form of the Islamic Credo:

25

'God is God, Mohammed is his prophet,' he enters Paradise
before an Arab.

'The Roumis,' they say furthermore, 'are superior to us
in many things; but they are always afraid of death.'

Touggourt, 9th April

Arabs are camping in the square, fires are being lit;
almost invisible smoke floats in the evening light. We were
at the top of the mosque when the muezzin climbed up to
chant the call to prayer.

The sun was setting, as if for ever, over the interminable
and exhausted plain. The sand which long ago had grown
pale, has become darker than the sky.

We had suffered from the sun all day and we found the
coolness of the evening delicious. Children were playing in
the square and dogs were barking on the terraces of the
houses. Above us the voice of the muezzin filled the little
cupola which crowned the minaret; his voice, sounding one
single prolonged note, seemed the echo of a great bell; then
it stopped suddenly and left a void in the air.

Owing to the extraordinary drought, all the cattle have
died this year and meat has become so scarce that people are
reduced to eating camel.

Leaving the town, you can see, under a small roof of dry
palm leaves, one of these enormous beasts, cut up; its flesh
is violet and covered with flies the moment one stops chasing
them away. In these lands the flies are as countless as the
seed of Abraham. They lay their eggs on abandoned carcases, sheep, horses or camels, which are left to rot in the
sun; the larvae feed themselves there in freedom, then,
transformed, make for the towns in swarms, in hordes. You

swallow them, inhale them, are tickled, worn out, wrapped round by them; the walls quiver with them, the goods on view in the butchers' and grocers' shops buzz with them. In Touggourt the merchants with little palm-brooms try to chase them on to their neighbour. In Kairouan there are so many that the best thing is to leave them alone. The merchants give up driving them away until a customer asks to see their goods. At our arrival our carriage was enveloped in a cloud. At the hotel the plates and glasses were protected by metal lids, which were never removed, never lifted, except at the precise moment of eating or drinking.

M'Reyer, 11th April

Wondrous chotts, fringed with mirages; – from the height of a sandy hill, after the immense expanse of the desert, you think: 'Hallo! The sea!' A vast blue sea with skiffs and islands, a sea which one hopes is deep and at the thought of which one's soul is refreshed! – You approach, you touch the edge, and the blue abruptly disappears – being no more than a reflection of the sky on a salt surface, which burns the feet and hurts the eyes and which gives way beneath one's steps, a fragile, thin crust on a sea of moving mud which swallows up the caravans.

At the officers' dinner the major next to me talks to me of the South. He had lived for a long while at Ouargla. He had even been in El Goleah and remembered the soldiers' marches through the sand. Often, amidst those shifting sands, burning and vibrating in the sun, a kind of queer giddiness seized them at feeling ceaselessly under their bare feet the ground giving way; even when they halted and remained standing, the swaying would continue and the ground would still seem to be slipping away from them. Then sometimes, in the midst of these grievous sands, they came upon a narrow vein of limestone, a cohesion of some kind, hard and just wide enough for each soldier in turn to place both his feet a moment on it, and on this narrow ledge of resistance snatch a few seconds to recover himself.

To punish a soldier they make him 'follow'. To march at the rear of the company is killing; those in front cannot trouble themselves about the laggers. Thus sometimes men drop out . . . stagger, fall, are swallowed by the desert. The last men run in the choking dust raised by the company over this ground, which is so soft, and all the softer for having been trampled by all the others. If anyone falls behind, it is all over; he sees the others moving away and rests; the birds which fly behind the marching battalion pause, wait, – then approach.

Often in this sand crystals, formed of gypsum, fragments of 'spear-heads', glitter like mica. On the road to Droh we found stones which, when broken, appeared transparent within and as if empty.

On the road to El Oued we picked some of those strange mineral flowers called 'roses of the Souf', formed of a little conglutinated sand and, like the sand, grey.

Biskra

The sounds of the negro drum attract us. Negro music! How often I heard it last year! How often I got up to follow it! No tones, only rhythm; no melodic instruments, only instruments of percussion; long drums, tom-toms and castanets . . .

28

'*Florentes ferulas
et grandia lilia quassens*', castanets,
which sound in their hands like the rattling of a heavy
shower. In a trio they execute real compositions of rhythm;
uneven rhythm, with strange staccato syncopations, which
rouses one to madness and sets all one's flesh a-quiver.
These are the musicians who play at funeral, festive and
religious ceremonies; I have seen them in the cemeteries,
sustaining the delirium of the paid mourners; in a mosque
at Kairouan, inflaming the mystic madness of the Aïssaouas;
I have seen them beating the time for the dance of sticks
and the sacred dances in the little mosque of Sidi-Maleck;
and I was always the only Frenchman to see them. I do not
know where the tourists go. I think official guides prepare a
selected Africa for them in order to rid the Arabs, friends of
secrecy and quiet, of the importunate, for I never met one
of them near anything of interest and, most fortunately,
only rarely in the old villages of the oasis, to which I went
back every day, until at last I startled no one. Yet the hotels
are full of travellers; but they fall into the clutches of the
quack guides and pay dearly for the faked ceremonies that
are got up for them.

29

There was not a single Frenchman either, last year, at that extraordinary nocturnal fête which I witnessed almost by accident, being attracted simply by the sound of the tom-tom and the ululations of the women. The celebration was in the negro village; a dancing band of women and musicians was coming up the main street, ahead of torch-bearers and a group of children, who were laughing and leading by the horns a big, completely black he-goat, covered in stuffs and jewels. It had bracelets round its horns, an enormous silver ring through its nostrils; it had neck-laces round its neck; it was clothed in a tattered piece of crimson silk. In the crowd that followed I recognized tall Ashour; he explained to me that that goat was going to have its throat cut during the night to bring luck to the village; but first it was led through the streets in order that the evil spirits of the houses, who stand on the doorsteps, should enter into it and vanish.

Negro music! How often, far from Africa, have I thought I heard you and abruptly all the South was re-created around you; even in Rome, Via Gregoriana, when the heavy wagons, passing at daybreak, woke me. Still half-asleep, I could for a moment be misled by the muffled bumping on the paving – then, for a long while I lay grieving.

We heard the negro music this morning, but it was for no ordinary celebration. They were playing in the inner courtyard of a private house, and at the threshold some men wanted at first to push us away; but one or two Arabs recognized me and protected our entry. I was astonished, from the start, by the large number of Jewish women gathered together there, very beautiful and richly dressed. The courtyard was full; there was scarcely any space left in the centre for the dance. The dust and heat were suffocating. A bright beam fell from the bay above from which, as over a balcony, clusters of children were leaning down.

The staircase leading up to the terrace was also crowded with people, everyone attentive, as we ourselves soon became. In the middle of the courtyard there was a large copper basin, full of water. Three Arab women got to their feet; they cast off their outer garments for the dance, undid their hair beside the basin then, bending down, spread it over the water. The music, already very loud, swelled; letting their soaking hair drip over them, they began to dance; it was a savage, frenzied dance, and nothing can give an idea of it to anyone who has never seen it. An old negress presided, leaping around the basin and, with a stick in one hand, struck the sides of it from time to time. We learnt later, what we were already beginning to understand, that all the women who were dancing there that day (and sometimes there are so many of them there that the ceremony lasts two days) Jewish and Arab alike, were sick people, possessed of the devil.

Each woman paid in turn for the right to dance. The old negress with the stick was a renowned sorceress, who knew the exorcisms; stirring up the water in the basin, she called upon each demon to leap in upon which, there and then, the woman was set free.

It was the beautiful Jewess Goumarr'ha who told us all this, but unwillingly, because of a last vestige of belief and because she was half ashamed to confess that last year she too, her body horribly contorted with hysteria, had taken part in the dance 'hoping to find in it relief from her ills'. But, thereafter, she had become much more ill and when her husband learnt that she had danced

31

at this witches' Sabbath, he had beaten her for three whole days to cure her.

. . . The dance grew more violent; haggard, distracted, seeking unconsciousness of the flesh or, better still, the loss of all sensation, the women reached the crisis whereby, their bodies having escaped altogether from the control of their minds, the exorcism could operate. After that immediate exhaustion, sweating, dying, in the prostration following the crisis, they hoped to find repose.

At present they are kneeling in front of the basin; their hands clenching its sides and their bodies swinging from right to left, forwards and backwards, swiftly, like a furious pendulum; their hair lashes the water, then bespatters their shoulders; with each thrust of their loins they utter a deep cry, like that of woodcutters felling a tree; then, abruptly, they collapse backwards, as if in an epileptic fit, with foam on their lips and their hands writhing. The evil spirit has left them.

The sorceress then takes hold of them, lays them out, wipes them, rubs them, stretches their limbs and, as is done for hysteria, seizing them by the wrists and drawing them half-upright, presses on their belly with her foot or knee. Today, they told us, more than sixty passed through her hands. The first ones were still writhing as others were already springing forward. One of them was small and hump-backed, clad in a green and yellow gandourah. She jumped about like the fairy in I don't know what fairy-tale. Her flashing black hair clothed her entirely.

. . . Some Jewesses also danced. They leaped uncontrollably, like delirious teetotums; they only took one bound and fell back directly, distracted. Others resisted longer, but their madness was getting the better of us; we fled, unable to endure any more of it.

32

'Who invented music?' Athman asks. I reply: 'Musicians.' He is not satisfied; he persists. Gravely I answer that it is God.

'No,' he says at once, 'it is the devil.'

And he explains to me that for the Arabs all musical instruments are infernal instruments, except for the viola with two strings, the name of which I cannot remember, with a very long neck and a body made out of a gutted tortoise. On these the singers in the market-places, the poets, the prophets and the story-tellers play using a little bow, and accompany themselves; sometimes so sweetly, says Athman, that a gate in heaven seems to open.

These singers and poets intrigue me. What do they sing? And the goat-herds in their dialogues with the flute? And Sadek with his guzla? And Athman himself, unaccompanied, or with Ahmed, each on horseback, at Touggourt? I listen, but am unable to make out a single word. When I question Athman, he replies: 'But no, it's not phrases; — it's just poetry!' — By dint of persevering, I succeed during these last few days in getting him to transcribe and translate some of these songs. They are the ones the singers in the market-places sing, sitting on the ground or at the entrance to a café, and to which a group of silent Arabs around them listen, or which they sing to themselves in the loneliness of their long treks. I do not know whether they will please anyone who does not know the country; I hardly dare say that I find them very beautiful or that I think the oral tradition of this Arab poetry, ancient and modern, worthy of a place in folklore. Here are two of these songs; I give them just as Athman gave them to me, altering nothing but the spelling:

33

I

For two years I have ceased from making love and say I am
    religious.
I have made my journey to the North; I found at the
    festival Baya . . .
She put on the comb and the earrings.
And the dagger, with the mirror . . .
Her hair falls on all sides,
Weighted with gold, well-arranged.
No one can buy her.
Only she or I . . .
– The young women have asked for a few coins –
And I, weak (I am poor),
Tomorrow I shall sell some sheep
For the lovely ones with their well-cared for rings.

II

Today, as she passed she turned away;
With a golden belt, its fringes on her thighs hanging –
– The thing that makes me suffer is her immaculate white
   dress –
I shall spend all night in running,
And it is I who make her dogs bark.[1]
If Ramadan[2] were a man,
I myself would break his knees,
But Ramadan has come from God,
I and you, we accept its sufferings.

[1] Love is very difficult amongst us, says Athman, explaining the poem, because the women are guarded by dogs and by their whole family.

[2] Ramadan is the forty-day fast; as much a fast of love as of food and drink.

For M. A. G.

I am copying out here, I don't know for whom else but you, these half obliterated notes. It was for you I wrote them during the endless tedium of the road, after I had left you at Biskra. That sort of charabancs, which carries the mail between Biskra and Touggourt in four days, passes the hotel well before dawn. Again I see your farewell, on the terrace, in the night . . .

I

Tuesday, 5 o'clock

Still in the oasis. – A subdued brightness, so faint that light seems almost shadow, and shadow depth. An early morning moonlight into which the dawn will melt.

36

A cemetery beside the road – where Athman's parents rest in the icy peace of the nights. The white tombs of the marabouts alone reflect some light; beyond them the other earth-coloured tombs indistinctly mingle their dust with the night. Palm-trees fringe the cemetery; at their feet the water of the seguias flows under the moon with a scale-like glitter. Not a song, not a scent, not a whisper; the grave poetry of this place, of this hour, is composed out of the deadly desolation.

The road crosses the village. Everything sleeps. In the clay cinder-grey houses, not a lamp, not a fire.

Do you remember that in our last journey here, at this hour and at this spot, a tiny owl on the dilapidated wall of the mosque was mewing; it was not disturbed by our approaching, but gravely stared at us, staring at it.

Now the last palm-trees thin out; and the equivocal illusion of life which the sleeping oasis offered vanishes, abandoning us to the desert, to the night, to death.

And yet, far off, at an immense distance, three or four fires, – nomad encampments, caravan-halts.

Not a cloud in the blue sky. Soon dawn will break. It looks, violet and sad in the East, as if it were a bruise on the night.

A caravan comes past. The moon, almost at its peak, gives each of the camels a short unassuming shadow. – It is cold. Athman, in Arab fashion, before sleeping, thrusts his enormous turban deep into the three hoods of his burnouses, huddles up, curls into a ball, becomes a pumpkin like the Emperor Claudius.

The plain – which the salt whitens – glimmers faintly under the moon. The smooth silver-frosted soil with magnesium in it or sodium, I don't know which, seems liquid. And above it, here and there, a bunch of lentisks, a tuft of meagre rushes.

Not a cloud. Here is the dawn. From the blueness of the still cold night to the red fringe of the sands, a prismatic colour-scheme of the day is revealed, but in more delicate and subtle tones, yet as precisely graded as that of a perfect rainbow; and over the marvelling earth comes a resurrection of colours. There is in this a total absence of art, a beauty purely and solely natural.

This will only last a moment. Already all subtle nuances are being effaced; there must remain nothing in space but brutal gold and blue.

But before the sun appears, once again the sky is suffused with a strange pale orange light, into which the sun soon advances, red and flat and soft like molten iron on an anvil.

7 o'clock

A flight of cranes in the golden sky forms a throbbing oblong cloud. Another smaller flight follows the first. They draw near; we can count them: there are thirteen. These two flights each pass on our left. In the science of augury what does this omen signify?

8 o'clock

As far as Saada we met with no signs of life beyond imperturbable caravans. Yes we did, – two jackals. The first one, fearful, fled at our approach. The other stays rather near us, motionless and hidden behind a low bush; only its pointed muzzle protrudes.

38

Dawn over the sea never seemed to me so splendid as this. Whilst sands redden and quiver, waves remain frozen.

Then the desert stretches on obstinately changeless. Pale clay, a little stony, in which a scrubby vegetation, reddish and round, checks the sand, lifts itself above it and looks, on this smooth expanse, like an abundant outbreak of warts.

Between Saada and Chegga we met nothing.

Chegga, 10.30

Breakfast – on a three-legged table – in the blazing sun, which has already begun to beat down fiercely. Two starving cats squabble over the remains of the cold chicken and sardines. Near us, in front of a wretched hut, where three poor Arabs shelter, a woman in a saffron rag washes a skinny girl of five, standing up, quite naked, in a black cauldron. Not a flower, not a blade of grass to give the hut a little smile.

He who does not know this country must first of all picture to himself: nothing. To the right, a hut. Nearby, some dismembered carcases – carcases of camels, one presumes. To the left, a company of camels; some camel-drivers, who water them at an invisible spring. Behind the well, which is the source of the spring, nothing; all around, nothing; sunshine; an avalanche of sunshine.

We go near the spring. For what? The trapped water flows into an orchard where twenty meagre palm-trees wilt. A donkey with a raw hide grazes at the foot of one of them. It would appear to be grazing the sand. The coach is harnessed, we start off again.

39

For more than two hours the same road has been unwinding monotonously in front of us. – A little fine sand coats the road now. The wheels sink in; the horses toil; we get out. The sun beats down. The plain receives too much light and appears, as far as the eye can see, leaden; all colour-tones are killed, but if you turn round, keeping the sun behind you, the tones revive, and the colour-relation between the low dunes and the sparse vegetation decking them is ravishing. I do not know the name of these plants. Their minute contracted leaves are of a silver, ash-grey green, exactly similar to the green of olive-leaves.

Kef el Dorh'

The land slopes abruptly down to the chott.

There was a time when I dared not admit to myself how little refuge and nourishment art can find on this soil. I needed to pretend it was beautiful before daring to admire it so passionately. It was in the days when I willingly still confused art and nature. Now, what I like in this land is, I am well aware, its very hideousness, its intemperate climate: what compels all art *not* to exist . . . or to take refuge elsewhere.

Here the impotence of the painter is conclusive; and his obstinacy in refusing to acknowledge it amusing. In the desert, one should content oneself with the education, the exaltation, I mean, which it offers, and know how to make one's dispositions accordingly. It is nothing other than this, I suppose, that a painter like Monet must have taken from here. The analysis of his craft, of his perception; the simplest possible understanding of each tone in itself, of its relations and its possible importance; the fading of all planes, the disappearance of reflections, the absence of variegation, the exposed nature of the surroundings. He must, on returning to his own country, have acquired – from the interaction of tones, from the resources within each of them, from the available reflections of surfaces, from the general atmosphere, – an understanding both more masterly and more spontaneous, a kind of revelation.

M'reyer

. . . where we arrive at night-fall. Bordj; vast courtyard, but how can I sufficiently suggest its desolation? It lacks everything; effortlessly it is immense, for nothing here is cheaper than space.

The moment one is outside the bordj, the night seems so huge that the bordj seems tiny. Never had I seen so many stars. Wherever the eye rests they prick the sky. Barking of dogs . . . an indefinable anguish takes hold of one; – one is ill-equipped to ward off emptiness; one feels everywhere the desert is giving way.

Lost in the night, we hunt for the village our carriage had passed before pulling up at the bordj. It is far away. We hear snatches of a barrack-room song and meet four soldiers, who come up to us and offer to be our guides. We leave them as soon as we are in the village. It is cold. In the middle of the street, – if you can so call the channel that runs between the houses, – half-naked children are feeding palm-leaf fires, beside which some old men are warming

41

themselves. The flames flare up for a moment, crackle, then die down, leaving nothing but a dull ground-glow. No music; no games; some almost lightless Moorish cafés; a few smokers in front of their doors, half lying on mats or on nothing but the bare ground.

And now that we have gone for the third time the whole length of the only two streets in the village, and that the fires are all out, and that we have put to flight, like flocks of wild birds, everything young and charming that was warming itself, now that the peace of this too queer place has been spoilt, – what are we to do? – but go back to the bordj through the oppressive solitude of the night.

II

Wednesday, noon

Bands of grey rose from the South. For two hours the sky was entirely covered with clouds; then, again from the South, blue sky reappeared. Now, once more, not a cloud from one end to the other of the entire heavens.

We are in sight of Touggourt. The sun, as it sinks, reddens. The sky is a perfect blue, a blue washed with gold at its edges. The approach to Touggourt surpasses all my memories. – On the horizon to the left the delicate line of the oasis, prolonged from M'garine, resembles the coastline of a bay, and the sea of sand, on which we sail, seems to break there. To the right, nothing; golden sand lost in the sky's golden shimmer. Before us, imposing Touggourt.

Slow-approaching port! While still far off, all one sees of it ahead, lifted almost out of the oasis, like lighthouses, are two bizarre minarets, outlined in black upon the sky.

The sun meanwhile disappears. To the East, the sand, for an instant rose and green, becomes in a trice delicately livid, infinitely pale, exquisite beneath a rose and lilac sky . . .

43

RENOUNCING THE JOURNEY
1903–1904

I was of an age when life begins to have a more dubious taste on the lips; when one feels that already each moment drops from a slightly lesser height into the past.

Obsessed by the yearning for this country, which flared up in me every year towards the autumn, and wishing to be cured finally – pro remedio animae meae, *I planned to write a book on Africa.*

I worked all summer from my recollections. Hazy recollections lacking vividness, and I could get no further with them. I worked in vain. I recalled nothing of the country but

its delights, which was precisely what drew me to it again . . .
I decided to go back a last time, under the pretext of record-
ing exactly each particular flavour.

When, for the sixth time, I took ship for Algeria, the book
I hoped to bring back was to have been quite different from
the one I offer today. The most serious economic, ethnologic
and geographic questions were to be raised. Certainly they
fascinated me. I took note-books with me which I wanted to
fill with precise information, with statistics . . .

Are those note-books, really, the ones I present here?

Back in Normandy, I sought at any rate to shape them
into a more homogeneous whole. But when I re-read them, I
realized that spontaneity was perhaps their only merit, and
that any work on them, however slight, could only spoil
them. – I publish them, therefore, almost without altering
a single word.

ALGIERS (FORT NATIONAL)

Tavern Gruber. – From this hot, harshly-lit room, in which I dine, I can see on the terrace thirsty people sponging their faces; a pavement; a balustrade; then the night's abyss: the sea.

Friday morning

Frightful night; heavy air; my sleep, in spite of my fatigue, torn to tatters by fleas, mosquitoes, bugs, and the uninterrupted din from the shipyards.

In bed by eight, at ten I get up again, maddened with thirst; while there is still time, I rush on to the quay for ice-creams and beer.

I got up at six o'clock, absolutely incapable of further sleep. Not a breath of air. Scarcely any lessening of the heat after the pantings and prostration of the night.

My room, at a corner of the hotel, opens on to a high terrace, faces the town and dominates the port. Above the sea, on the sky-line, a thick bank of haze and steam hides the sunrise; it is like solidified heat.

The sirocco is blowing. It is suffocating. Am on the terrace, bare-footed; the flag-stones are hot. Everything is tarnished, the most delicate whites look sullied. One feels that as soon as the sun has cleared the wall of mist, the heat will be staggering. And with one leap the sun clears it.

This morning the market; no longer in the open air, alas! but under cover. Bright-coloured fruits, tomatoes, aubergines and some marvellous roots, the colour of clay and skin, which, however, one must bring oneself to recognize and call potatoes.

Moorish bath; the same one in which, *due anni fa*, in a rage Gheon joined me. How it rained! Now how fine it is! – But the clientèle has changed, alas! Everything strikes me as less new here; I am less young.

In search of a room, at Mustapha. I look at everything, hunt everywhere. I thought before arriving: 'any bed, anywhere'; and everything seemed possible; – now I begin to feel myself impossible everywhere.

And the flies!

Then, down to the Botanical Garden; across it in a hurry; at a run to the beach . . . Oh! to bathe! . . .

Tepid water; fresh breezes; restfulness; languor.

Botanical Garden at night. The bamboo-walk already dark . . . I took a stroll in the evening, at the hour when, in the avenue of plane trees, one could hardly distinguish the

trunks from their thick enveloping creepers . . . Back to
the Gruber, where I write this. I am going to bed.

But I shall have seen those giant morning glories of which
you spoke. Twining stalks, flowers of a violet-purple hue or
paler, always facing one; their cold colour can dazzle! . . .

Giant lantanas; oleanders; hibiscus with glazed, green
leaves and crimson blossoms. – To sleep.

Saturday

A hundred and two degrees in the shade. It has not rained
for six months.

The strange and exhausting fact is that it is hotter by
night than by day. For during the day if there is sun, there
is shade, cooled by a breeze from time to time. But after six
o'clock in the evening, the wind drops; an even, dull heat
settles down. Everything thirsts. One dreams of bathing, of
drinking. One says to oneself: 'I shan't be able to sleep tonight'; and one begins to prowl. Even the sky looks impure.
Without any anticipation of a storm, everything is tarnished
with heat, and reminds one, beyond the favoured Sahel,
of the enormous continent all ablaze.

I drink; I drink! How I drink!!

I sweat; I sweat! How I sweat!!!

I think of the parched oases . . . there, I will go! – Oh!
obscure and leaden nights above their palms!

I have not yet been able to discover from where this smell
of sandal-wood rises or falls; it floats beneath the branches
in the square, it envelops and fills you.

An hour before sunset invisible birds set up in the fig-
trees of the square such a shrill chirruping that the whole
tree is drunk with the sound.

48

17th October, Saturday

The activity in the port does not stop for one minute during the night. The terrace outside my room overlooks the port and all through the night, sleepless, I listen to the shouts of the dockers, the thump of the bales, the whistles and especially the unbearable creaking vibration of the winches.

This morning I am setting off in search of the pure, fresh mountain air; I start for Tizi-Ouzou at six o'clock.

Woken at five, in the dark. The unbroken grey sky augurs a burning day.

The haze of heat is so low that even from the Botanical Garden one loses sight of the upper town.

Here is the golden beach where I bathed yesterday. Oh! how refreshing the sea would be at this moment! Hardly the heave of a wave on the beach, and as though the sea breathed . . .

This third-class carriage is like a lazar-house. In one corner a bundle of rags: it parts when the guard passes and discloses inside an unbelievably pustulous face; the

49

ticket-collector does not press. – A little way off, an Arab
vomits.

Fair at Tizi-Ouzou

Torrents of dust on the road. Sellers of little heaps of figs
beside the fields of fig-trees. Merchants of water-melons,
pastèques. Extraordinary animation; I have seen its equal
only in Brittany on the road to St. Ann on the day of the
great pilgrimage.

Crowds. They all seem of the same social class. Ali and
Saïd are the only handsome ones; but even their good-
looks are lost in this homogeneous mass.

Saïd recognizes me no doubt, but hardly betrays the fact.
With Ali as my guide, I find him again at the centre of the
market. He is wearing, like his brother Ali, the huge
pointed Kabyle hat either on his turban or slipping back
over his neck and shoulders. Saïd has shot up, has the hand-
somest eyes in the world, hard features, a cruel, mocking
mouth and an uncandid expression. His dainty dancer's feet
have grown bigger and lost their distinction through walking; they were made to tread on lawns and carpets only.

Their father, Akli, wears blue spectacles, looks more and
more like a bird of prey or someone ready to rob you. We
drink tea. I leave Akli with Saïd and go off again with Ali,
who wants to show me their home.

I find myself in a square unfurnished room. A lamb bleats
in a corner; on the ground Ali's wife, a child of sixteen,
perhaps even less, suckles a sickly child. In front of the door
Ali's mother feeds the youngest son. Within these narrow
walls the three generations live side by side. Still more
children, brothers, sisters, cousins . . . I am offered fried
honey-cakes.

50

Little loaded donkeys, sometimes bearing an old Arab; they are grey, their limbs are stiff, they crop on their way fallen acorns, horse-dung. Little grey cows with stiff limbs . . . The carriage jostles everything; we drive through.

Fine trees; some clothed to their crests in vines. The ground falls away, but the trees spring high; nothing supports them in the azure air.

The grapes have been picked. I thirst for even a single pomegranate left on a branch.

I have made this long climb by short cuts and almost entirely on foot; it is very beautiful. But I should have preferred the segment of the wild pomegranate I picked off the tree to have been less unbearably sharp. The fruit had cracked in the heat and was showing its almost-white seeds. Yet there was still some juice in it. But I realized that a thirsty Arab would have ignored it. Even in its wild state the flavour of the fruit is noticeable, but patient cultivation is needed to sweeten, soften and temper it. Nevertheless I persisted, bit again, and retained for a long time on my gums and my lips a sensation of aromatic astringency and a sort of tightening tastiness.

Fort-National, Sunday

This morning, when I woke, there was the same mist as a year ago. What a solace after the excess of sun! I imbibe it voluptuously.

One can hear, as soon as the nearby noises die down, the shouts from that far-off village. I have just been there. One would have thought it was populated by goats. As the village is on a rocky height, there is but a single street along the crest; as soon as the gaze, through an opening in the houses, crosses a courtyard, it plunges into the void. The walls are white-washed; the roofs the colour of raisins. The men are ugly; the women extremely beautiful. A whole population of children follows me. – How cool the air is tonight! How pleasant it is to be alive! What charm there is in the blue sky! A noticeable dampness chills you with well-being. What is everything smiling at? Why does everything tonight seem as happy as I am?

It is not the late autumn which is despoiling those high trees of their leaves. Grass is lacking to satisfy the cattle's hunger, and every bit of foliage helps. This is what cows, goats, donkeys and oxen browse on here; the Kabyle's hand shakes down towards them this airy pasture.

I am reminded of that slim shepherd in the gardens at El Kantara, who, from the top of an enormous apricot-tree, rained down leaves for the benefit of his flock. Already touched by the autumn, as soon as he shook the branch, they fell. – It was like a golden shower which lay on the earth a moment, instantly to be licked dry by the goats.

I should like to linger another day or two in this country; but even should I live here thirty years, I should find nothing to say about it; though as picturesque as you could like for an adventure novel, one cannot depict it as it is; one can only attempt to describe or talk about it. I am honest about this perhaps, but as an artist I must admit my impotence.

This morning it drizzles and rains; every Arab covers himself with a sack. Then the cloud is torn apart by the pressure of the overflowing azure. And this street which serves as a square, this terrace and balcony fill with idyllic animation and laughter.

Acacias border the square, then a steep drop hides everything but the far-off mountain opposite. – These idle children are not good-looking, but very graceful. A deliciously cool breeze blows softly. – The crests of the Djurdjura are in shadow.

After dinner, yesterday, I went out too late; the Arab town seemed already dead. The four or five French cafés, all too brightly lit, shamelessly glared into the night. I climbed the suspicious-looking steps which lead, behind the cafés, to the high quarter of the town. The Jewish shops are shut; everything is dark; only at the top of the steps a meagre gas-lamp; I sit down on a seat made up of planks. And no sooner seated, I hear at the turn of the street the grating of an Arab guitar. There is a Moorish café over there; I notice now its feeble glow in the night, which parts the darkness hardly more than the low sound of the guzla rebuts the silence. – Shall I go and look? To see what? Nothing but a miserable hovel, a dozen Arabs lying down, a musician most probably ugly . . . Better stay here. Let the night enter into me, insinuate itself with the music . . . An Arab leaves the café, comes towards me, thinks me drunk; and indeed I am.

Monday evening

Returned to Algiers.

How fine it is! Not a cloud in the sky. The sea is calm; invites one to a journey. The sirocco has dropped abruptly; and with it the temperature. It is hot, but less overpowering. The shadows are bluish and light and the air seems filled with a light of its own. It is delicious, subtle, almost fresh; you might say, joyous. – I think of the oases . . . I leave tomorrow. How beautiful their swaying palms will be at night! I will think no more of the past . . .

The indefinable colour of those grapes tempted me; I could not resist buying some. For threepence I got an enormous bunch.

Nothing can describe that bunch's hue; it was violet and at the same time golden; it was transparent yet appeared opaque; the grapes were not close-clustered; they were covered with a thick bloom, sticky, tight-skinned, bursting, almost hard – and so sweet that I could only eat four, and then gave the rest to the children.

BOU-SAADA

I

Wednesday, 21st Oct., in the train

I have brought several books with me; but I have tried
in vain to read. This country holds my attention. There is a
latent drama here between brute matter and life, a drama
for the intelligent observer, full of anguish. For it is not a
question even of cultivation, but simply of existence. Here
everything invites death.

A topsoil, thin as the side of the hand.

Then, becoming shaly the ground flakes; it is not rock any
longer, it is cake, really. And there, more and more con-
stricted, grow pine trees without thirst.

55

The wind blows from the South; the sky is overcast. It seems now to be an unbroken reflection of the grey shale. No doubt it will rain soon . . .

Oh! to be a plant in order to relish, after months of scorching heat, the voluptuous delight of a little water.

From the train

Once again the pines have come to an end; cleft and ravaged, the ground shelters a few oleanders in its secret folds. And now some yellow or green clusters of a hairy vegetation appear, and to crop it, a few goats.

In sign of salutation to the passing train, the little Kabyle shepherd displays himself fully, completely naked under the gandourah he lifts. He seems a goat amongst his goats, and not to be told apart from the flock.

Bordj-Bou-Arreridj

Little room with white-washed walls, I dread exceedingly your bugs! – What do your fringed curtains matter, your floor of broken tiles, your patched counterpane, your stained and spotted carpet, they don't matter! . . . But in the corner opposite the bed, that battered divan; a bad sign! And on the marble mantelpiece those artificial begonia-rex in painted pottery vases . . . I prepare not to sleep a wink all night.

Over a small Arab shop-front is a sign-board with the words:

COMMON LUXURIES

56

Through this splayed cutting of peeling monochrome rocks, the old, rickety coach descends the river-bed. In the way of this land, the water flows towards the interior to lose itself in the chott.

Round a rocky bend an oasis suddenly appeared – not of palms, but of fig-trees, tamarisks, almonds and oleanders. Then, giant apricots, a windmill, some flocks, some Arabs. And lengthily the oasis stretches on, following the oued, now insinuating itself between its narrow banks, now, owing to the extreme aridity of the soil, so strangled that it seems, for the bird that flies above, almost no more than a green thread; then, again, widening, spreading, lifting itself, to make one think: a little sun, and its mantle of shade will be filled with charm.

But since this morning the heavy, dense, unbroken grey sky sheds over this golden land monotonously a fine, insignificant drizzle. It is not enough to quench the earth; it is enough to deaden and tarnish its colour.

M'Silah

Eight years ago, whenever I saw Arabs in prayer, I went out of my way not to pass between them and Mecca; I was afraid of cutting the thread.

O perfumed gardens of M'Silah! I would have offered you my song earlier, had I but known you then. The running water of your seguias rolls the tipsy tortoises over . . . The frail pomegranate-branch bends low beneath the weight of fruits so heavy . . . An oleander in flower! Let us go closer.

Is it possible that eight years have passed already since the evening when my friend Athman, in the matchless little garden at Kairouan, taught me that garden is *Dj'nan* in Arabic, and if it is lush: *Boustan*.

... It is at this pre-vesperal hour when the voices of the birds are impassioned, that I want to return here and feel the fullness of indolence . . .

Towards Bou-Saada, Friday

Above us a continent of clouds which at last after two hours we pass.

But the sun, overcast since dawn, holds before it for a long time still, as it were, an eye-shield. It is past eight before it succeeds in looking over it. The first rays are icy; instead of warming, they freeze one.

7 o'clock

In front of us, those far cerulean mountains, which we are approaching slowly, slowly become less blue, seem to be floating less insubstantially and to present themselves with more reality. And lengthily the questioning eye listens to the way a blue tone passes into rose, then from rose to fawn, to flame.

Endless chott of the Hodna, expanse of fretted clay. Far off, here and there, a few tufts of rushes, like warts. Still farther off, water; at least, its fallacious appearance.

9 o'clock

Cloud! who this morning rose like a tuft of tow off the horizon into the sky, is it you who, grown huge like the cloud of Elijah, now invade the sky? – Alas! alas! you will take your abundance of water farther on, shedding none of it on this land, and thirsting plant and beast will receive from you no more than the coolness of a little shade at noon.

11 o'clock

In the excessive light the mirage now expands. Dancing waters, shady gardens, palaces: it seems, in the presence of this inexistent reality, that, like a barren poet, the impotent desert dreams.

1 o'clock

For at least two hours the horses have been pulling and toiling through the sand, and the oasis of Bou-Saada, which we could see at the start, hardly seems to have grown any larger yet.

A big, fat Jew from Constantine, on business in the South, pulls out of his bag in the second hour of the journey Lichtenberger's Nietsche and, turning to me, who can do nothing about it, exclaims: 'For my part, Sir, I understand one's dying for an idea!'

II

Letter to M . . ., Saturday

. . . 'It is a great disappointment to find that Bou-Saada is on this and not on the other side of the mountain; its desert lies to the North and is merely the interior plain of the Hodna and its not very unusual chott. Between the *real*

59

desert and me, I can *feel*, as much as see the thick confused massif, an extension of the El Kantara mountains. The oasis, set in a notch of the mountain, therefore sits facing the North and meditates on the Known. Here, no more returns of caravans, no more departures on the fatal invitations of the desert. – The oasis, full of charm, like that of El Kantara, has not the tragic grandeur of so many others, which seem to encroach on death.

'. . . This morning, up at five, I left the oasis and walked in the ravine, drawn irresistibly in spite of everything towards the South. The countryside became more and more rugged and rough; a cold wind blew, incessant as a river-flow. The sun remained hidden behind the mountain. And as soon as I had rounded the mountain, the heat and the sun became so strong that I only wished to return. I had already gone a long way, having walked straight ahead steadily for more than an hour. I would have liked to pick you those oleanders whose last flowers were fading, scarce already, but some still very lovely; I had imagined they would have a very delicate scent of peach, and was disappointed that they had no scent at all. The sound I made walking was all dispersed in the silence; stopping, I could hear nothing but the piping of a curious russet bird which was following me; it was the colour of the rocks. – I should have walked on – for what? Yet I would have liked to walk on . . . Anguish is in ourselves alone; this country is, on the contrary, very serene; but the question grips us: is it *before*, is it *after* life? Was our earth like this – or will it become so? A chaos of rocks. – How beautiful they are beneath the sun!

'One must have had experience of the desert to understand what "cultivation" means . . .'

60

Bou-Saada, Sunday

. . . He replied: 'I am looking after the water.' – Sitting
on the edge of the seguia, the child was keeping watch over
a small sluice which carried down to his garden the thin
trickle of water, to which he had a right until three o'clock.

At three the child got up, set the water free, and then
led me into his garden. His father opened the gate; we
went in. The watering over, a pernicious coolness reigned
there. Still, we sat down. His youngest brother, whom I had
not yet met, offered me figs and dates. – I would have liked
to be able to tell stories to the child; his large amused eyes
listened to me, even while I was saying nothing. – The
juice of the syrupy figs had made my fingers sticky; I
wanted to wash them in a puddle; but, so minutely irrigated
was the ground beneath the apricot and fig-trees, that there
was nowhere the size of a shoe on which to place one's foot
without ruining some tiny dyke or bruising some vegetable.
After causing frightful damage I sat down again, then
remained for a long time drinking the shade in, tasting the
coolness, without thinking of anything any more, without
speaking.

61

On leaving the Ksar and without descending as far as the oued, I followed a narrow canal of limpid water, which, halfway down, winds through the oued's gorge, passing round the rock-face. On one side of it ran my path, almost lost in the rock; on the other side, below it, an uninterrupted tangle of oleanders, the highest branches of which dipped into the canal, and the lowest into the oued. The bed of the oued was deep and night dug it deeper still. The water, scarcely flowing, lost itself amongst the pebbles, and reflected in pools the linen-grey sky. On the farther bank, gardens; and opposite, dominant, enormous, the rough-flanked mountain reddening from moment to moment, turning finally the colour of a fiery pomegranate; it seemed hot and ready to burst. At its feet the palm-trees in the garden were black.

Having with a leap cleared the rock in the shadow of which I had been walking, I found myself suddenly beneath the open sky. The sun had vanished long ago, leaving a sunset of great splendour; it was the reflection from this that was kindling the mountain in front of me. Three light clouds, without impairing the purity of the sky, took on the shining beauty of ornaments . . . This is the hour, I thought, when the blue smoke of El Kantara makes the oasis remote and vaporous. Bou-Saada is not so lovely, but the Ksar, filling with clamour now, seems at the very moment of its entry into night to become impassioned, as do the African sparrows in the branches before they are stroked by sleep.

III

Between Bou-Saada and M'Silah, Monday

Impossible to write this morning; the air is icy. From five until eight I struggle to make my cocoon of blankets airtight. The sky, impeccable yesterday, is overcast and immediately after sunrise takes on the hideous colour of a grey ointment.

This morning I am full of hate for this country and make frantic efforts to exile myself from it. I listen to myself recalling the Third Symphony of Schumann. I repeat, too, the Sonata to the Grand Duke Rudolf, in C minor; but here and there the violin part eludes me. When at last, the temperature allows me to put my hands out, I take Virgil from my bag and re-read the Eclogue to Pollio.[1]

Nothing of all this satisfies me; this morning I would like to go to the Louvre, and re-read La Fontaine.

Two Basques, big fellows, tanned, swarthy and seasoned, are the drivers this morning. I am alone with them in the very primitive delivery-van which serves to carry the mail. The other travellers' places are taken up by barrels, sacks and packing-cases. The Basques lash the horses, toiling through the sand, less with the whip than with the voice. – '*Maquereau, la Carne, Cornard, Bijou, la Flemme, l'Espagnol*' – there is a special tone for each. Michel, even more than his nephew, knows how to play on the resources of this language; one is deafened. From the second stage on, when the uncle takes the reins and the whip in his hands, it is one thundering fire of gutturals.

[1] In my opinion, it is the least beautiful. There are hardly any of those languorous, liquid, perfect verses, which are the delight of the others.

63

Overwhelmed with fatigue, my head splitting, I leave the front seat and, right in the back of the antique carriage, slipping in between the piled-up sacks, I vanish inside my black overcoat and absent myself.

We started six gazelles. Dissolving in the russet sands, one can pick out only their fleeing white rumps.

I learn, while talking with them, that my Basques come from Setif. No matter.

After a period of giddiness, the huge plain seems to distort itself before one's eyes. One would think it was crossed with eddies, and flowing; then, in stretches, swollen; the swirling soil is full of currents and waves, and the suffering eye grieves at being unable to establish a perspective anywhere.

The wind is rising; the canvas flaps; a squall. Courage! poor crew! only five hours more to shore!

Our northern skies have not known such thickness of cloud. Upon so huge a thirst how huge a weight of water will descend! – to transform at once that thirst into drunkenness and the clay plain into a swamp.

Six hours of riding yesterday; ten hours in an unsprung old carriage today. Tonight, not the smallest muscle in my body but cries out. As soon as we arrived, I collapsed on the first bed, and from three o'clock to five departed this world, after a meal of four eggs. Tomorrow, starting before dawn, I must travel till nightfall.

Profiting by the last light of day, I follow up-stream the course of this rushing seguia, in the hope of finding there one of those black tortoises, which so amazed me when I saw them from the carriage on Thursday. – But nothing; and suddenly I found myself very far away, very solitary, in the most formless of plains over which the most inhuman of nights was advancing.

Tuesday

A sudden wind has driven the storm away; hardly did one heavy shower fall on the arid Hodna; but the sky remains leaden and dirty. This morning, this land does not awaken in me a single word of praise. I stare with indifference at the dreary rocks, at the oleanders bordering the bed of this oued, which enchanted me on the way out. Cowardly, I changed from the top of the carriage, this morning, to the coupé, to be able to read more comfortably. Whence in this moth-eaten stage-coach, a little more comfortable, nevertheless, than the Saada delivery-van, comes this smell of soured soup? Is it from the pitiable traveller, who shares the coupé with me?

Doubtless, elsewhere as much as here I could see a cow put out its dribbling muzzle to drink, – but in the absolute bareness all around, I look at it more lengthily than I would elsewhere. A child leads it. It is thin; it stands after drinking, there, in front of the water, stupidly, waiting for the child to lead it away. For it no verdant field; its hunger will find till nightfall only hollow stalks of maize, which sparingly the wretched child will stretch out to it, the wretched beast.

ALGIERS (BLIDA)

I

Algiers, Wednesday, 28th October

The sky is sad; it rains, but there is no wind. From the top of the terrace I look out over the sea; as far as it stretches, not a wrinkle. It is from over there that you will come; my eyes picture the path and furrow of the boat; would that they could plunge as far as Marseilles. Ah, may a clement sea bear you! and may the heave of the waves be pleasant to you! – I dream of the days when one said: 'May a light wind swell your sail!' . . .

A sun-ray falls on the Admiralty wall which instantly becomes white and dazzling. But the sky remains burdened with water. What clouds above the Atlas! It is on such a day as this that it indeed seems to bear the weight of the sky.

Those three little children on the steps of the stairs leading to the port – they are dividing between them not a fish but a fish-bone, God alone (Who feedeth the fowls of the air) knows where they must have found it. There is still a little flesh on it, close to the head; that is where they are scratching; each one gets a scrap as big as a pea.

A few steps lower down an old Arab, two fingers thrust down his throat, makes himself sick. What horror can he have swallowed, to have to vomit it up? He is starving.

. . . But out of these varied elements a new race takes shape, proud, voluptuous and daring. It seems to spring from the Andalusian, the Basque, the Provençal, the Corsican, the Sicilian, the Calabrian: it is the Algerian. One is quite astonished to hear him speak French.[1] – When young, he is handsome, often very handsome; his complexion is not glowing, but of an olive hue, his eyes are large, full of languor; fatigue with him is mingled with laziness and seems the lassitude of love; he keeps till a late age his mouth half-open, the upper lip pouting, as do very young children.

The salvoes of the guns, which the Russian ship and the French ships are this morning exchanging, panic the garden birds. It is as if a tempest suddenly swept them away. How many there are! They swirl above the square, and when they fly near me it is with the scream of a squall.

The gunfire ceases. On to the soothed trees the birdflight falls like a calamity.

Absence of the fear of death is the defect of Arab art. They do not recoil from dying. And it is of the horror of death that art is born. The Greeks, who up to the threshold of the tomb denied death, owe their art to their effort in protesting against it. If the Christian religion had achieved

[1] Moreover, he speaks it very badly; but he speaks equally well – or equally badly four languages.

68

its aim, the certainty of eternal life would have denied art
(I say art, and not the artist – artists are legion amongst
the Arabs). It would have flowered neither in books, nor in
cathedrals, and Francis of Assisi might perhaps have thought,
have sung, his 'hymn to the stars'; he would have left it
unwritten, lacking the desire to perpetuate anything mortal.

Friday

Last night at the theatre Jean Coquelin. More from idleness than desire I went to hear him in the *Bourgeois
Gentilhomme*. He represents a stupid, conceited ass, sure of
himself. I think the important feature of Jourdain, beneath
his transparent bombast is his anxiety – the anxiety of one
whose temperament remains quite different from the part
he assumes; he is constantly afraid of not making the correct
gesture. That is what the actor should show. – Reflected on
this, as if I were not in Africa. – *Le Dépit Amoureux*, which
was played first, though rather badly acted, enchanted me.

Saturday

Frightful squall. Hail, wind, thunder, lightning . . .
'There's too much of a hubbub,' as M. Jourdain said
yesterday.

Monday

Some despairing Russian sailors – lost in the side-streets
of Algiers, not knowing a word of French or Arabic, when,
three times running, they make signs to be shown the way,
are led back to the harbour and to their ship. In despair the
Russian sailors hold out to anyone they see a blank sheet

69

and a pencil; a postman passes: – 'But for Heaven's sake write the address of a b . . .!' I tell him, foreseeing that, once again for the fourth time, they will be led back to the harbour.

This stale and musty smell of urea, belches and luke-warm dirt that floats on the stagnant air of the Moorish bath . . .

There are days when one asks oneself whether it is the meat that is too tough or the knife that does not cut. In any case, the result is the same: one has no more appetite.

Tuesday

I do not know what name to give this prolongation from the mole to the lighthouse, a sort of stone jetty of huge cubes of rubble that a cement-like putty conglutinates; then, still farther beyond the lighthouse – to the farthest reach of this artificial promontory, on to that last block, which the first assault of the huge wave whitens, a narrow refuge, by which, when night falls, one imagines one is entering the very heart of the sea. A red buoy, which marks the entrance to the port, lifts or falls. The sky is stormy; the sea black; the cavernous gaps between the blocks at every swell of the waves boom. And yet not a breath of wind; each wave is enormous, without a crest, broad and deeply hollowed. At times, in a contraction of the rock it chokes; the spray spurts towards me. Oh, that a sufficiently strong wave might carry me away! Oh, to be numbed in the green bitterness of the flood! . . . Far off, the street-lamps of the city, lulled by night, light up. Drunk, deafened, dizzy still from listening too long, watching too long the waves in this recess of the mole, where I have been soaked – suddenly here is T . . . who comes up to me. During one hour I pretended to listen to him, and I was compelled to agree with him, just because I understood him so imperfectly.

That great ship – doubling the mole, one would have thought it was surrendering to the waves and would sink. Yes, the last wave, as the ship turned, almost laid it low, but then, lifting it one last time, carried it triumphantly into port.

And towards nightfall the sea on the Agha side transmuted itself into that strange oriental green, which I admired at Malta and Tunis.

– The moon, brushing aside the clouds with a thrust of rays, travels across an open field of azure. The sea grows calm, or am I mistaken? – so much tranquillity does the silvery oil of this nocturnal light pour on it.

Wednesday

I will not go and look for anything by the sea; my eyes flee the horror of those clouds, being chased to the North by a gust of wind. Already Apollo fills the sky, exultant above the high town. O laughter of the houses! Azure depths! Up there, as soon as evening falls, I shall climb – yes, up to the foot of that rose-red wall, the gayest of all, the highest, which nothing separates from the sky but in the distance a floating branch of eucalyptus, rocked by the wind. But, like the object of our desires, at close quarters will you appear so beautiful, happy branch, whose leaves today's light washes better than yesterday's heavy shower?

71

No; it is no use. One can revisit the same place twenty times – never again with a sense of novelty. One looks more attentively; one sees less. One understands better perhaps . . . but the entrancing astonishment has vanished.

Thursday

It is going to rain again. The sky is heavy, the air is clammy. In such weather as this I can scarcely write. It is curious how much shadow the tiniest cloud in the sky spreads over my thoughts . . .

Walked through idleness, through sadness, along the quay, to the quarter of Saint Eugène. A black sky; rain over the sea, which the wind is driving towards us. Heavens! Into what have they changed Algiers the white? That once light avalanche of snow . . . into a sump. So much snow here melts into mud. Upon stinking refuse, hovels haunted by a people in rags. A stagnant pool where joyless children, bare-footed, paddle. Then already, for these are only passing horrors, the yet more sinister horror of yards, of wine-vaults, of warehouses.

But today this landscape exalts and supports my sadness. Night falls. Still following the quays, I listen to myself reading Virgil; I look and listen to the wave, whose spray the wind drives towards me.

Thursday night

From this gate which faces it, from the Admiralty mole, I picture the old Algiers as some prints still show it, bathing its bare feet in the sea. These monumental quays, these buildings, behind which the Mosque of the Fisheries is buried, these hideous warehouses, these wine-vaults, these black vessels, – my eye suppresses them and puts only greens and whites in their place: – the narrow strip of land, connecting the islet on the mole with the town, reveals beyond it another glimpse of the sea; where the rock stopped, the earth was very green. Some houses by the water's side, but few. To reach the sea, a ravine. A path leading to the sea drops down from some white houses, leaning over the edge of this ravine . . . I imagine it by night and, as it leads to the fountain, I see women following it. The fountain is near the sea where feluccas come and go . . .

Alas! alas! white-gleaming Algiers is no more.

What are those children looking for, like hens, in that compost heap? Neither for pearls nor millet-seeds. The rags which so poorly cover them have covered so many others so many times, that these remains, these leavings, this refuse, to which so many others have helped themselves, may help them yet.

There was up there, in a not very secret street, but in a secret tuck of the street, a tiny café . . . I see it. – At the back of that café, on a lower level, was a second room, narrow, it seemed, and receiving its light from the café; from where I was, I could not see the whole of it; it vanished into a recess. At times an Arab stepped into it, who had come straight from the street and whom I did not see reappear. I suppose that at the far end of this retreat a secret staircase led to other profundities . . .

Each day I waited, hoping to see something more. I went back there every day. I went back in the evening; I went back at night. I lay half stretched on a mat. I waited and watched, without moving, the slow disintegration of the hours; there remained at the close of the day a cinder of time, subtle, bitter to the taste, soft to the touch, rather like the cinder in that hearth between the tiny pillars, over there, close to the mysterious lower recess on the left – where, at moments, moving aside the ashes, the café-keeper revives a dying ember, beneath the cinder-heap . . .

At times, accompanying himself on the 'guembra', one of the Arabs chants a song, slow as the hours. The hashish-pipe goes round. Obstinately, despite myself, I watch the thick darkness over there, the wall-mat of the retreat, into which I had seen that suspect descend . . .

Three months later, the police had closed the café.

One night, I was offered the pipe, with a gesture so friendly . . . Ah, the significant puff I inhaled! – It is better to smoke hashish on an empty stomach, I am told; I had eaten . . . I felt at once as if a fist had struck me hard on the nape of the neck; everything somersaulted; I shut my eyes, then felt my feet rise above my head, then the ground fall away, flee from beneath me . . .

A few seconds later I was in a sweat, a cold sweat; but already there remained nothing of the nausea, abominable at first, but a dizziness, – dare I say pleasant? – of one who, weightless, is no longer quite sure where he is, and floats, floats . . .

Another evening there entered abruptly, pretending to be drunk, a tall, strong Arab with a cunning eye and a drawn knife. He played with it, tested it . . . It was not one of those small knives of the Roumis; it was a large, powerful

cutlass, as lean and sharp-pointed as its master. Drunk he
perhaps was a little; but not as much as he pretended.
Everyone knew him and spoke to him. Above each one he
twirled and twisted the blade. Finally, it was my turn. All
the rest was a game, I said to myself, in preparation for
what follows. Control yourself! . . . Yet I run a risk by
appearing to defend myself . . . But if I don't defend myself
in any way, what will happen? – Already I imagine beneath
the recess horrible, hungry depths . . . But I did not budge;
merely gripping my heavy cane, almost on high, with
both hands . . .

Nothing happened at all. The bogus drunkard went
away. Again the little café was quiet, and again I was able
to watch in freedom the patch of matting in the recess.

II

I went to see him then at Blida, as I had promised him
I would on the boat between Marseilles and Algiers. He was
in the infirmary, for he had caught a fever in the first days
of his service.

In his *tirailleur's* uniform he looked very unwell, and his
eyes were brighter and more disquieting than ever.

'I thought it would be different,' he began, 'and if I had
known . . . I am bored. That is what is making me ill; I am
bored.'

'But what did you expect, then?'

'A life which would not be the same every day. I don't,
myself, want to live long, you see; I would like – how shall
I put it? – to live for a very short time as fully as possible.
You don't understand that, do you?'

'Oh, come now!' I said.

'Look here! Will you give me a great pleasure? Find a
way to get me . . . a little kief. They say it's marvellous. I
would so much like to taste it! But the niggers all refuse
to bring me any.' (He called without distinction every
Arab 'nigger'.) 'You've never smoked it?'

'No,' I replied.

'You'll bring me some, won't you?'

'You'll drug yourself.'

'I won't . . . Besides, I don't care. People like me are of
no use in this world . . . Yes, I remember what you said on
the boat; don't repeat it: it irritates me. Bring me some
kief, please.'

'It's not sold any more. It's forbidden.'

'Oh, you'll find a way to get some . . .'

76

'You won't know how to smoke it.'
'I'll learn.'

And in the Rue des Coulouglis I met Kabisch. Though we had not seen each other for three years, we recognized one another at once. O walks on the mountain! Monotonous singing in the garden; whisperings in the Sacred Wood full of moonlight; dances in the little clandestine café! With what regrets mingled with what desires will my memory of you survive! . . .

'Kabisch, where can I find some kief?' I asked.

I followed him meekly into three Arab houses; for it was not enough for him to slip under my coat the little green packet which the first merchant had slipped into his burnous; it was necessary at a second merchant's to select expertly the bowls for the diminutive clay pipes; at a third, the stems. I took some for ****; then I took some for myself also.

Trading in kief is forbidden – or clandestine, if you prefer it. Since the police have closed all cafés with a smell of kief and claim to detect in kief the smell of crime, it is only smoked in secret, and as its penetrating fragrance betrays it, it is little smoked now. There was a time – what shall I say? – when with its narcotic odour all Blida was perfumed. Now anyone who returns after some years' absence, marvels and asks of Blida what it is that has disenchanted her. – The Rue des Coulouglis has no scent any longer.

In the street of the Ouled, each woman before her door, as before a niche, laughs and offers herself to the passer-by.

But the loveliest thing I saw that night (in a passing, fleeting glance, while a woman calls to me) was through that open door, by which in one bound my desire enters, a garden, dark, deep and narrow (and there my desire wanders) which I can scarcely discern and in which a cypress-trunk I see plunges into water I suspect – and, farther off, lit from the other side, luminous, hiding a mysterious threshold, a white curtain.

Blida barracks

'. . . When I ask where it comes from, they say they can't smell anything and don't know what I mean. Nevertheless, myself, I know very well that I am not imagining it, that smell . . . Now! Don't you smell it rising? No, that's not the smell of a flower. I call that the smell of the soil.'

And indeed I smelt rising, falling towards us, a heady exhalation, hardly a perfume, yet like that which in spring-time Japanese lacquer-trees release.

'Oh well!' he added in confusion, 'when I smell that at night, it's too much for me; I have to go off into a corner to . . .'

November 10th

So long as Blida has not become incurably the small, mediocre, provincial garrison-town, which it obstinately makes every effort to appear, I shall, lovingly, beyond its decompositions, compromises and decays, and amid the frightful commonness of its patient progress towards banality, seek, as in muddy water for a spangle, some trace of its defunct enchantments, from its loves of yesterday some lingering delight.

Last night I made a round of the Moorish cafés in the town without succeeding in hearing, with however little loveliness, the song of the *guzla*. I name incorrectly that hollowed tortoise with its abdomen of resonant skin, on which two stretched strings vibrate. One should say *guembr* or *gnibri*. What can avail Blida without scent and without song? Of its youthful loves is there nothing left but debauchery? – Not one of the *gnibris* yesterday had strings. Had the child who led me from café to café not been beautiful, I would have wept. It was already bad enough that he bore the absurd name of Abd'el Kader.

They gave me in the first café some of that biting ginger tea, which one would imagine originated in the unquiet and unhealthy East. I would like to describe, but do not know

how, the charm with which the very bareness of that room touched me. No pictures, posters, nor advertisements on the walls; white walls; not far off, the confused din and cries from the Rue des Ouled, heard through the walls, gave a rarer and more voluptuous quality to the silence here; no seats: just mats; on the mats three young Arabs lay.

What did this retreat offer them, that they should prefer to the amusements in other places, to the laughter of women, to dances, the absence precisely of all those things? . . . a little kief. The tiny pipe, from which each one in turn drew but a few puffs, was passed round. I did not dare smoke, fearing, not drunkenness, but a sick headache; however, in the cigarette I rolled I let Abd'el Kader mix a little kief with the tobacco. And perhaps this mild whiff helped me to a sense of real well-being. This well-being was not due to the satisfaction, but to the effacement of desire and the renunciation of everything. The door giving on the street was shut, and the noises outside moved farther away. Oh, to linger here! . . . This is the hour . . . Abd'el Kader, leaning towards me, points out to me, solitary ornament on the white wall, hooked to the middle of it, a hideous, shapeless puerilely-daubed doll, and says in a whisper: 'The Devil.' – Some time passed. We left.

In the second café, with the sickeningly sweet tea was mingled a taste of liquorice.

In the third café, a very old spectacled Arab was reading a story to a whole awe-struck crowd. And, fearing to break the thread, I refused to enter, but remained outside on a bench, in the night, a long time . . .

Hammam R'hira, 11th November

The earth, drunk with a shower, dreams a sudden spring.
And now there are everywhere, hugging the soil, without
leaves, over-scented white dwarf-narcissi; minute peri-
winkle-blue rods of what I think must be grape-hyacinths;
pink stars of frail belladonna lilies, which look rather like
our meadow-saffron; – and all of this very small, timid,
close to the ground, crowded together. Here, then, is the
best that the rain's gentleness can draw of grace from an
ungracious soil!

The forest of Hammam R'hira reminds me very much of
the forest of Esterel near Fréjus. The same perfumed dryness; lavender and burning resin. The same pointed, dry,
gleaming foliage, which the autumn never reddens and
never yellows. A blue sky.

81

In this ravishing, flashing, radiant weather, everything this morning looks glorious. The azure air seems fresh and new. I feel it filling me with health and vigour. I shall walk over the mountain – over there, high up, without a goal, without a guide and without a path.

Hammam R'hira, 12th November

It was hot; towards midday I felt thirsty and had a wish to bathe, not in the modern establishment's well-equipped swimming-bath, but in the old, almost forsaken one, which a few poor Arabs in the Hammam below still frequent. A descent from the hotel garden leads to it. One hears rustling waters. The air is soft, full of shade; beneath leafy canopies a green, refreshing night trembles or slumbers . . . Here is the old Hammam; beside it a café; on mats three Arab cripples drowse. I step into a courtyard where a cock crows. A staircase leads to the swimming-pool.

Noiselessly I push open the door of the high, vaulted chamber. I face a sheet of suffocating, transparent water. It falls from the high vault to the middle of the pool in cascades, and from all over the pool mounts to the vault again in steam. A narrow curb, level with the pool, runs all around it and frames it. The water is hot . . . No one in the obscure chamber; thick steam; but, from far up, through the split vault: four marvellous sun-rays, blazing a hole at one bound through the suffocation, dash themselves against the livid wall.

Blida, Friday 13th

On that abandoned bed I breathed for a long while afterwards the green and earthy smell the faun had left behind him; then, in the morning, waking at the break of dawn, I darted out into the delicious air.

III

Algiers, Saturday 14th

Hail! smiling morning. The full laughter of day can come: I am ready.

The sea, on a level with the sun, holds itself upright before me, like a wall of light, like a pane of iridescent mother-of-pearl, which the delicate hardly distinguishable line of the hills, softened by the mist and almost spongy, frames and divides from the sky. In the port, still filmy and filled with the smoke of giant ships, a trembling flight of little boats scatters, rises towards the open shining sea and, at moments, with oars spread, skims, as if through liquid light, and seems to glide on wings. And, facing the sun, on the land, between the hustling quays and the sky, the city laughs.

My eye, which for lack of sunshine during the past ten days was fasting, wakes to the sun, looks about and observes with appetite.

From the top of the street of the Kasbah an orange begins to roll and bounce; a little girl darts after it; the orange flees . . . If one of the French boulevards does not stop them, they will roll right down to the sea.

Sunday, 11 o'clock

There remained on the wall's length nothing more than a narrow space of shade, which the sun little by little was strangling; just enough to harbour my thought. But already of thought I had no more than would just fill that narrow, shrinking space. Soon on the wall there would be only heat and light, in me only feeling and fervour.

Monday

We had seen at the market in the square pomegranates as rosy, pimentos as green and purple, sweet onions as glossy, but there, in the sudden seclusion of the alley, in the shade, each fruit gained a new brilliance.

I admire how slender a profit can satisfy the Arabs. I dared to bargain over some fruit. Squatting on his heels

84

in the middle of the tiny stall, a child was selling them. One could have had the whole stall for a few pence; for a few farthings more, the salesman.

I should like to be hungry enough, one day, to wish to eat some of those chick-peas which the merchant would take straight from the platter and pour into a straw-coloured cornet, stained with brine. –

. . . to be thirsty enough to drink from the neck of the copper urn which that woman, whose face I cannot see, rests on her hip and would tilt towards my hot lip. –

. . . tired, in this booth, to await the night and be, amongst those the night gathers, indistinct, just one amongst others, simply.

. . . oh, to know, when the heavy black door in front of that Arab opens, what will greet him, beyond . . .

I wish I were that Arab and that what awaits him were awaiting me.

The outskirts of Algiers, Tuesday

One heard, every time the rickety carriage stopped in the plain, the approach of one of those formless silences, which only occur in the very hottest weather. It descended upon one like a woollen blanket, in which a thousand flies hummed. One felt well; one felt at ease. One stifled.

It is you, aromatic forest, I chose this morning, wishing to breathe your air until the evening. O immense walk! happy weariness of the flesh. – The moment one steps aside a little from the secret crease in this ravine, where water one hears but does not see gurgles, what is still called forest becomes nothing more than stunted undergrowth; rock rose, lentisks and dwarf palms. One slope of the ravine was in shadow and, despite the great heat, such a chilliness lingered in it that the grass, as Ronsard would have said, was *pearled*. And in a hollow, which the rock-fold sheltered, the air was blue and my breath formed a cloud. Higher up amongst the lavender I sat down; I pressed against the icy rock the palms of my burning hands. In front of me, on the other slope, a prey to the sun, everything was on fire. I gazed at the white flocks on the distant crests, and, at times, helped by a breath of wind (so huge was the surrounding silence) I heard the shepherd's call and, at times, a stronger breeze snatched a scrap of song from his flute.

Towards the close of the day, on that very same rock, I came and sat again. Now the sun was setting it ablaze; it wrung all perfume from the dry, exhausted grass. In front of me, on the other slope, the shadow grew; and when it had reached the flocks, these, abruptly heading downwards, towards the peace of night slowly picked their way.

Algiers, Wednesday

In that crowded restaurant, where one eats worse than anywhere else, which is saying not a little for Algiers, – two Italian mandolinists throughout the meal pinch and scratch. The air is filled with joyousness and mediocrity.

Restaurant de l'Oasis, Friday

At the centre of the sideboard, in parsley, on a plate, an extraordinary crustaceous monster couches.

'I have travelled a great deal,' says the maître d'hôtel; 'but I've never seen that except in Algiers. In Saigon, for instance, where there are crayfish as big as . . . (in vain he searches the dining-room for a suitable comparison) these are unknown. And even here they're quite unusual. In three years this is only the second one I've seen. Sea-grasshopper, Sir . . . because of the shape of the head; just look at the profile. One would swear it was a grasshopper's head . . . Yes, certainly, Sir, excellent; something like that of a crayfish, but much more delicate. Tonight we're cooking her. If you come to luncheon tomorrow, Sir, you could have a taste.'

The sea-beast, with six people around her and talking of her, holds her tongue. She is grave, immobile, ungainly, the colour of dross, expressionless; she looks like a muddied rock.

'What? Not alive!?' With a thrust of his thumb the maître d'hôtel drives in one of her eyes; the grasshopper, with a sudden start, lashes out fearfully with her tail and sends the parsley flying from the plate; then settles down again.

Throughout the meal I stare at her.

87

This morning she is still there; reigning over the parsley, on her dish.

'We didn't cook her last night,' says the maître d'hôtel, 'she was still so full of life; I thought it would be a shame.'

The outskirts of Algiers

I would have preferred it to be more idle, this square beneath the fig-trees, which a fountain's clear sound enlivened . . . But today amid the noisy outbursts of the vendors the sound of the fountain is lost; flocks fill the air with dust, and down the four roads, which here meet, the white Arabs eagerly press towards the market.

Yes, I thought, this is the reason why only those rose-bushes exposed to the torpor of winter produce the finest roses. On this rich, hot African soil the smallness of those flowers, which at first astonished us, their tightness, their strangled beauty, comes from the fact that the vigorous rose-bush never ceases to bloom. Each flower opens without eagerness, without premeditation, without expectancy . . .

In the same way the finest flowering of man demands a preliminary torpor. The unconscious gestation of great works plunges the artist into a sort of stupid numbness; and not to consent to this, to take fright, to wish to become creative again too soon, to be ashamed of one's winters, that is the way – by craving for too many – to strangle and make abortive every flower.

The pump, which a mule was turning, no doubt feeds this square cement pond, green with abundant moss.

Level with its edge there was water which at first sight seemed black and which one did not realize was deep and clear, until, leaning over it, one distinguished at the bottom a carpet of dark fungus. A shadow, extraordinarily thick, weighty and silent, fell across it from the opaque, glazed vault, which a fig-tree formed above it. The distant trunk threw its branches towards the humidity, and from the middle of each branch there hung a mop of tiny roots; one was aware, vegetally, as one approached the water, of the effort made towards it by this imminent suction; for, no sooner in touch with the damp earth or the water, than the root, having attained its goal, held fast and imbibed for the parched tree the increase of sap it craved. The root then thickened, formed a stem, then a new trunk; on it the tree supported the weight of its branch.

I do not know where to place in my paragraph that monstrous toad which, flattening itself on the water's face, blocked a root-cave, as black and warty as itself. I did not

distinguish it at once; as soon as my stick touched it, pustules broke out all over it. Certainly it reigned over this tranquil water. Prodding it with my stick, I saw its yellow paunch. It fell back into the water, askew. Black fish, which one did not notice at first, fled.

27th November

Three weeks ago I should have been able to leave Algiers more easily; already I have formed habits here, little roots . . . a few days more and I would no longer be able to tear myself away.

And every year, for so many years now, I have resolved never to return . . .

But the longing for this garden, at night, – for this midnight garden, where every night I came . . . Oh, how shall I endure it?

BISKRA

28th November, 6 in the morning
Departure for Constantine

These mountains above Blida have never seemed to me so
beautiful as at this very early hour, when the sun hidden
behind them still, still casts no shadow. Beneath a shivering
dew the plain Mitidja was becoming iridescent; it seemed as
if the azure, issuing from the mountains' flank, was flowing
towards it. It was not a mist even; it was an airy blueness;
yes, over the plain all the air was filling with blueness, and
without losing its transparency appeared all the bluer as,
above the crests of the mountains streaked with blood, the
pallid dawn was spreading.

The vast regions, which were parched last month and seemed russet-brown and bare, are tender and turning green now. Barley is growing and in the fields, where the earth has not recently been loosened, the ploughshare cuts with ease.

So these large, bare fields, I thought, will soon be covered with deep grass and the heavy spring breeze will roll across them. Every bird, every living atom will swell with sudden joy, open its quivering wings and sing. There will be the whisper and brush of light movements, amorous pursuits . . . Even the insect will have no illusion about the brevity of joy; the awakening of love and the embrace will be imbued with fever; almost at its birth delight will swoon, and already in the perfume of the flower there will be a hint of the flavour of the fruit.

El Guerrah, Sunday, 29th November

What wind! What cold! The sky is covered with clouds; they seem to me almost motionless, while a fierce whirlwind scatters the dust and smoke close by us. There is no tree for miles and miles around to prevent the wind from sweeping flat over the ground, whereas the clouds, piling high, provide an obstacle. And I imagine the absence of vegetation is another cause of the rigorous weather: as the sun's rays strike no absorbent surface and as all the reflecting surfaces are very nearly horizontal, the rays only develop their heat when they are almost vertical. And for the same reason this suddenly developed heat, with nothing to absorb it, can cease suddenly. Finally, the dryness of the air or the rapid evaporation, when the earth has retained some trifling humidity, conspires to make the transition from hot to cold almost immediate.

. . . Everything contributed to it: the novelty of the environment and in my own self, where all I discovered enchanted me; – and the craftiest means could not have provided such a multitude of virgin delights for my enjoyment as did my puritan upbringing. And then, precisely over there, I had the good fortune to fall ill, very seriously it is true, but of an illness that did not kill me – on the contrary – merely weakened me for a time, and the clearest result of this was to give me a taste for the preciousness of life. It would seem that a weakly organism is, for the absorption of sensations, more porous, transparent, sensitive and more perfectly receptive. Despite my illness, if not because of it, I was all welcome and joy. Perhaps my recollection of that time is here and there a little confused, for I have a bad memory, but from the bouquet of sensations, which I brought back from my first voyage, there escapes so keen a perfume still that at times it hinders my enjoyment of the present. I refrain from comparisons, however; but I do worse: I return to that country six times, claiming the past from the present and exhausting my emotion, requiring again of it that freshness which it owed in the past to its novelty, and finding year by year always less lively compensations for my ageing desires . . . Nothing equals the first contact.

Monday

Doubtless ten years ago the times of the trains were not the same, and I rather think that it was only at night that one arrived at Biskra – for, amongst my confused and painful memories of that endless journey (I was ill) one moment stands out nevertheless with extraordinary vividness:

After Batna the sun set; as one descends from the uplands, the air grows warmer hour by hour. (The last two days of the journey killed me.) – A halt in the night, which had already fallen. The station has the rather ridiculously poetical name, but which that first time set me dreaming, of Fountain-of-the-Gazelles. I open the carriage door. The silence is extraordinary, of a strangely unfamiliar quality. The soft air soothes one's eyes like collyrium. Nearby a toad's call, a single note, pure and bucolic, which later the Arab flute would recall. Through all my tired and drooping senses I drank . . .

Such memories poison.

Towards Biskra by train

Under a grey sky an expanse of grey water, the colour of rain; a stubborn wind wrinkles it; but there are no waves, for the water is shallow; at its edge it is no more than a dribble, a froth; grey sand mixed with salt prolongs it, mingles with and is hardly distinguishable from it; after that there is no more sand or water; but a pasty intermediate substance, with a thin coat of magnesium, white as the salt. A horse's imprudent hoof has left muddy holes in it.

I remember one day when this salt and water reflected nothing but the blue of the sky, and sky and water seemed to melt together in the distance, – I saw these banks aflower with pink flamingoes. The train passed close by them; a few flew away; it seemed as if the wind from the train lifted them; then, a few wing-beats farther off, indolently they let themselves alight again.

I re-enter the heart of my youth. I set my steps in my steps. Here are the charming banks of the path I trod that first day when, weak still, just escaped from the horror of death, I sobbed, intoxicated with the sheer astonishment of *being alive*, of the enchantment of existing. Oh, how soothing were the palm-shadows to my still tired eyes! Softness of the light shadows, whisper of the gardens, perfumes, I recognize everything, trees, objects . . . the only unrecognizable thing is myself.

This garden in the hotel courtyard, which I saw planted, is already leafy, dense and tangled. It grows dark with shadows and mystery . . .

How pleasant it would be, were there not so many poor on the earth, to gossip quietly with some friends, this morning.

Beside this mill, so low that a few low fig-trees almost hid it, we liked to come and sit. Have ten years passed since then? . . . A little grey donkey brought the wheat and carried away the flour. Not far off there was a tent of nomads, whose children and dog we had domesticated. P.L. painted, and little Ahmed brought us eggs, then sat down beside me without speaking.

They have diverted the river from this charming spot; flowing out of the mill it ran past the foot of that gum-tree, which, deprived of water, now withers . . . Its shade was perfect . . . What demon leads me back here?

Extremity of the Oasis, beyond Guedesha

On this side the desert is formless. Towards the horizon it seems to curve upwards like a basin. The soil is sandy, ashen; some unknown sapless vegetation makes the earth seem at a distance clotted and scabrous. The sand glitters in the sun. A kind of continuous mirage blurs the perspectives; one cannot place any object at its proper distance – and, besides, as far as the horizon no object can be seen. On the right, a projection of the Djebel extends towards Tolga; the rock bursts open the coating of sand in places; seen from far-off it looks like an eczema . . .

I know however that when one approaches it this delicate sand is so charming to the eye that one cannot tire of watching the shadows fall on it, and so pleasant to the feet that I can remember taking off my shoes and climbing barefoot to the top of the dune . . . That was ten years ago. I was with Mohammed and Bachir. A snake, harmless, they told me, but terribly long, flashed away, like a whip, almost from between my legs . . . I remember the kind of person I then was . . .

From the top of the highest terrace, Friday

Darkness is slowly gathering over Biskra. Is it night falling already? Or is it that hideous cloud lowering? It covers the sky from one end to the other. It comes from the abysses of the desert, beyond Touggourt, from Ouargla, from the depths of innermost Africa; perhaps the steaming Great-Lakes have swollen it; it is full of menace and horror; it is yellow. It does not resemble those of our lands; I would like to give it some other name than 'cloud'. It trails along the ground, beyond the palm-trees; it hides the mountain from me. It is light; it is sandy-grey; at the same time it spreads uniformly over everything like a cloak whose top edge is just a little lighter through wear. The white of the

96

house-walls turns livid, and the pink of the tiles ashen. I think of djinns . . .

The firing of a cannon, marking the end of the fast, resounds.

Saturday

The cloud, like threadbare cloth, has given way at the horizon. Is it through that azure tear that the wind blows this morning with such overwhelming stubbornness? The sand blinds one; it is freezing. Neither coat nor burnous can protect one against this wind. Through the cloud the sun appears, silvery, flat and like a worn medal.

I intended to bathe this morning at the mournful Hot-Spring. But in such weather, across the desert – one would die of cold and suffocation and horror . . .

Come on, let's go.

O misery! O desolation! – I sit down, sheltered from the wind by a heap of fallen clay, sand and stones, beside the ruined bank of a leaden lake where the water under the thick reeds stagnates. And if only, while grazing his skinny goats, there came a shepherd-musician to sit here . . . I am alone. I search within myself, contemplating so much desolation, for a surge of vitality to awaken delight, to endow with a tremor of emotion so much death. – I remain here. The wind tosses the reeds. A hesitant sun struggles to smile at the desert and a silvery gleam lies on the crumbling salt, like paint on a corpse.

I would have liked to climb that mountain path, where only footsteps have worn the rock white. One can see it vanishing up the pass, whither? – An unbearably cold wind prevents me following it; I return to the Hammam and have a boiling bath.

At the Cadi's

The little hall opens on a level with the street; camels pass. In a sort of second hall, formed by an alcove in the first, in front of a tiny desk, the cadi. He speaks softly and a smile plays on his handsome face. In the first hall, separated from the alcove by a screen at elbow-height, Arabs wait. They are sitting on a kind of wide solid seat which runs round the four walls of the room and which only the openings of the door and the alcove interrupt; it is inlaid with bright green tiles; at the foot of the seat the babouches are placed. The ceiling is white-washed; the wall to half its height painted green. In front of me an admirable old man with a long beard and grey, blinking eyes; there is in his poverty a certain quiet dignity; there is just enough flesh on his body to lodge his soul. I admire against this green background the rich and becoming harmonies created by his grey-brown skin and the sober folds of his turban and burnous.

Athman, standing in front of the screen, which serves at the same time as a hand-rail, talks to the cadi, explains to him the very complicated business of the purchase of the house his mother lives in at present; on my advice he wishes to legalize the matter. The cadi listens to him without boredom, as he would to a story; now and then Si Malek, the vendor, interrupts; both speak softly. Other Arabs come in and begin their wait on the bench. There is an untiring patience in the air. Leaning against the door, a one-eyed child chants a religious litany; a pious Arab holds out a penny. Camels pass.

Yes, this garden is marvellous, I know – and yet I do not like it much. I try to find the reason why. Perhaps it is because of the very care with which it is kept up (not a fallen leaf in the sanded alleys); nothing to me seems natural here. – It is a work of art, you will say. – I grant it; but, in the same way, a lack of abandon, of ease in any work would displease me. Then again, I populate a garden at once, in spite of myself, with figures that fit it, whose bearing and sentiments are in harmony with it. So, I saw at the Villa Pamphili Van Orley bowing in his lordly robes, and Dante and Beatrice in the orchards at El Kantara. Nothing far-fetched in my choice: I see Goethe at Dornburg, composing *Iphigenia*; Tasso at Este between the two Elenors. Here irresistibly, I see characters from Jules Verne; they smoke *londrès*, they do not talk of 'francs' but of 'dollars', they have never read our Racine; they are always on the eve of

setting sail . . . It is true I also see the *Fortunio* of Gautier – or Stevenson, which is not unpleasant. I see also here Gauguin's characters; what surrounds me is their flora, artificially acclimatized; bamboos, cocoa-palms, monstrous fig-trees . . . By the inescapable power of suggestion, as soon as the most paltry palm emerges from the most trifling foliage, one dreams of some *other* country, where such vegetation would appear still more natural.

Why, of course not, sophist Maurras, it is not a question of cutting one's roots, and 'uprooted' has never implied that. The admirable thing is, precisely, that the Englishman, as did the Roman, takes his roots everywhere with him.

In Lady W . . .'s room, one feels one is no longer in a hotel. She travels with portraits of relatives and friends, a cloth for her table, vases for her mantelpiece . . . and in that common-place room lives her own life, in comfort, and makes every object in it hers. But the most astonishing thing is that she has contrived to create a society for herself.

We were four French families, each one carrying on its affairs apart from the rest; each one quiet, courteous, but, as it were, doing penance in the hotel. The English, numbering twelve, without having known each other before, seemed like people who had been expecting one another and had now met. Pleasantly untidy in the morning, pipe-smokers, busying themselves with different jobs; at night, wearing brilliant polished shoes, dinner-jackets, correct and 'gentlemen'. The hotel lounge was an easy conquest for them; it would have been presumptuously useless indeed to dispute it with them, so natural did it seem that they should take it over; for their part, they knew how to make use of it; we did not.

And, besides, as I have said, they formed a society, we did not.

I have only met two kinds of Frenchmen abroad (and usually none at all); the *interesting* ones, who isolate themselves, and never lose the feeling that *they are not at home*; and those who form groups, are noisy, common and repulsive. – Were they repulsive, these English people? – Certainly not! – Oh, on the contrary they were very fascinating; especially the three artistic young men, rather a group apart in the group. Painters? Writers? What matter – they read Stevenson and George Moore, and were the ones I would willingly have spoken to, if only my heart had not beaten so fast at the thought of doing so. Besides, what should we have said? – Again, I feel towards them a sense of manifest inferiority, and even though, as an individual with sufficient consciousness of my own value, I have enough pride to suffer in no way from this feeling, as a Frenchman it is intolerably painful to me.

Must I recall here one of my most mortifying souvenirs? I was travelling by train with P.G.; it was evening; we were not due to arrive before dawn; we were thinking of settling ourselves as comfortably as possible for the night, and so, fearing an invasion of passengers, we had retained with our bags, our coats, and our rugs, tolerably more room than was reasonable. From the two far corner-seats two English ladies watched us without a word. An Englishman arrived, inquired about empty places, took only one and settled in it. The train left. And then this is what happened. Slowly, irresistibly the two misses and the Englishman spread themselves, and finally it was they who had the benefit of the seats first reserved by us; and we could do nothing; first, because we had no use for the seats; then, because it would have seemed to us Frenchmen unseemly to stretch ourselves out, thereby depriving those two ladies of doing the same. We spoke English rather badly, a fact which our fellow-travellers quickly perceived and of which they took advantage to talk about us. We knew enough to understand that the Englishman was saying to the ladies:

'Amazing, these French! They always begin by taking up more room than they need. But they don't know how to keep it . . .' then he added, laughing: 'That's when the Englishman steps in.'

The broaching of this subject was the start of a noisy conversation which prevented us from sleeping for a long time.

Tonight, standing on the very edge of the terrace which projects into the sky, we watch the rising of the moon. – A dawn, a pallor above the mountains precedes it. The mountains there seem to swell gently. Is it a cloud enlarging them? – Yes; the dark shape expands, then, as if under pressure, bursts, tears and forms a crater out of which the moon, pushing aside the jagged edges, emerges and is freed. It is as plump tonight as an egg. Just a little longer and it will be completely laid. It swells all the time. How big it is! Already it would not fit again into the dark crater. How round it is! – What would you say if suddenly, with one bound, breaking away from the earth, you saw it hurtle to the zenith of space and burst – or, down the slope of the mountain roll towards us into the plain.

Sunday

Splendid weather. – Oh, I have not been alive for days! This morning through the shutters I felt the sun rising radiantly. I went out into the icy air. Everything was being born . . . There is nothing like the felicity of early morning. My joy does not grow little by little, hour by hour, throughout the day; it is already whole and complete on waking – all the keener when I have got up earlier than usual and there is a longer day ahead for it to fill.

Near the hotel the gate of the pleasant public garden is open. I go in; I sit on a bench. Frej', the husband of the lovely Jewess, Goumarrah', sweeps the paths, 'dresses' the garden. In front of me, in the pool full of plants, water splashes drop by drop on to a mossy rock. I write these lines.

No, the sky is still milky, almost white; I must see it perfect for my ecstasy to be perfect.

Sidi Taïeb is a marabout. His virtues protect the town. – As he is often seen with young women of easy virtue and seems to have a joyous disposition, I tried to get Athman to explain to me in what his virtues consisted. But on this subject Athman does not welcome jokes; and even though I mean to be serious, my question alone creates a doubt . . . Sidi Taïeb is an article of faith.

Sidi Taïeb enjoys the utmost consideration. This expresses itself in gifts. Sidi Taïeb is a sober man; he despises money; clothes are what he likes. The devout, who amongst us would ask for a mass to be said, buy a burnous for Sidi Taïeb.

Now, although he has many, Sidi Taïeb never changes his burnous. As soon as the last one he has put on is dirty, he slips another over it. One on top of the other, he carries the weight of a score. Nothing could possibly be heavier.

On certain fine evenings, – Athman has told me, – in front of a big fire in the square, Sidi Taïeb emerges from the heart of these burnouses completely naked. Most probably this is when the lice become altogether too troublesome. Some pious disciples, then, extracting the undermost burnouses, throw the three or four oldest into the flames where, crackling, the lice perish. Then Sidi Taïeb dresses again and new burnouses rain on him from heaven.

Under this weight he cannot walk; he rolls. One day I saw him moving forwards; he looked like Ubu going to war. – Another day, supported by two girls, doubtless sanctified by him, two Ouled in gala dress, he was following an excited procession on its way with music and a great hubbub to the tomb of Sidi Sarzour, and was laughing, staggering and reeling; he was like a drunken Silenus.

However splendid he may appear thus, I myself prefer him motionless. On his knees, seated, squatting . . . one can't tell; one sees nothing but a rotund mass, rocking from side to side. He remains thus till late into the night; in the centre of the square he looks then like the holy phial; he is shaped like a teat.

In the street of the Ouled a staircase and a courtesan's house have taken the place of the shadowy café where, my first year, I used to go to forget time every evening.

These two streets of pleasure are parallel, and so close to each other that more than one café opens on both; these two streets, intersected by three others, are not, as often happens, in a remote corner of the town, approached in tortuous secrecy; no, unashamed, they run into the most ordinary, central quarter, near the market. A public garden is a continuation of them; the air in them is not at all foul; it is air from the sea which blows across the perfumed garden. If everything debauched and dubious in the town roves there,

everything noble and pleasing roams there also. The crowd brushes shoulders without ill-feeling; the poorest mingle with the rich; the young with the old . . . everything blends. The most timid child passes by these prostitutes without looking away; the wisest old man also.

In a rather secluded café, sheltered from the noises of the street the same Arab, to whom I listened last year, reads Antar. By the entrance are a few benches; on the café-floor mats. In there a whole attentive white-clad population is lying down. Amidst so much soothing whiteness nothing shines, everything melts and mingles; the somnolent light envelopes everything evenly; it has the softness of water, flowing slowly, without reflections and without a rent in it. – The reader of Antar is very handsome; his voice has a sonorous, triumphal ring. Sometimes, lowering the book lit by a candle, he explains and comments on a verse. When he reads, he scans the lines with one hand; with the other, close up to the candle, he holds the book. Sometimes laughter shakes the crowd, like the laughter, I fancy, that shook the table of the gods on Olympus; it is some witticism of Antar's, or a striking feat of arms by some Arab. Subjected, fallen, the listeners find solace, respite and some element of splendour to sustain them in the account of their ancient prowess ... The reader's words fall faster, his voice rolls like a drum; one can hear nothing of the verses but their heroically resounding rhythms. How splendid they must have been, these people, in victory!

Abandoning the crowd and my obscure companions for one night, I go and sit with Athman in front of this smaller café, on what we would call the terrace, – which here is just a wooden bench and a badly lit table. Sidi M. joins us; he is an Arab from Touggourt, neatly dressed, eloquent, with a well-groomed beard. He knows the desert from the frontiers of Morocco to Tripolitania. He talks of In-Salah, of the Touaregs. His voice is musical; he pronounces each word so clearly that at times I think I understand him. Athman translates.

Sidi M. is a scholar; that is to say, on every subject he quotes a text; the more ancient the text the more it is venerated. He believes in every Arab fable; he pays no attention to the Roumis.

All the scholars I have met in Algeria are the same; and when Athman 'instructs himself', I know what that means; it means, instead of formulating questions, collecting forthwith an entire tradition of answers. And that is enough to fill them with self-complacency. – What in the Middle Ages was known as learning was no more than that.

106

'Have you read,' Athman asks me, 'in the Thousand and One Nights the story of the Erudite Princess? Well, you can see for yourself the learning there is in that!'

I question Sidi M. on the relations between the Arabs and the Touaregs.

'The Touaregs,' he answers through Athman, 'don't like the Arabs, and often attack them; the Arabs very much fear them.'

'But all the same one sees them in the towns of the Souf?'

'They accept,' he replies, 'the Marabout of Amich, because he performed a miracle against them. All alone, on his mare, he went forth to face the Touaregs who were mounted on eighty camels. The Touaregs drew their bows, but the arrows you understand, touching the mare, became soft at the tips and all fell to the ground. He, on the other hand, did not want to harm the men; but, with a single arrow, he killed sixty-five camels.'

He says further: 'Over there, those Touaregs know a country in a mountain, so vast, so vast that one can walk straight ahead through it for ten days; only one path leads into it, and only one man at a time can go down it. When all have entered, the last man rolls a stone across the path ... well, a stone about the size of that table; and then no one can see the road. That's why the Touaregs are not afraid of the French. – A Touareg told me this at In-Salah.'

On the denuded fig-trees still a few leaves remain; broad, flat leaves, of thick gold. Under the palms, in the dry shade they spread out, float, glide, you might almost say, – until the day when some shepherd, more active than the winter, finishes stripping the branches for his flock.

107

And once I have sung the perfume and the whiteness of it, what shall I have succeeded in expressing here of that night, which I would have liked to prolong until the dawn? – A waning moon shone high in the sky. The night before, full still, it did not seem so lovely; it had rained; only a few Arabs were to be seen in front of the houses of pleasure, only those who had not feared to come from their ancient villages along dirty roads and sunken paths. – This particular evening was soft and voluptuous, there was just enough water left on the ground to make it yielding, and to give the air, usually so full of dust, that light and bluish haze which deprived every object of its weight. And through this night air, harmoniously, a whole people were moving.

There, amidst so much nebulous whiteness, amongst so many shadows, a shadow myself, drunk without drinking, amorous without an object, I walked, caressed now by the moon, now by the shadows, hiding my eyes filled with tears and full of the night, and wishing I could vanish into it. – And at our chance meetings, sometimes I walked with Athman, sometimes with Ali; and with them I sipped, like a sherbet, the moonlight, now sad and now enchanted by all that their untutored natures still preserved of grace and of boyishness despite their increasing years.

Happy, too, to recognize the women by their voices; to smile or stop at their invitation; to see, in a sudden brilliance of light and sound from the cafés, so much roving mystery in sharp focus, the shadows take on substance, halt for a moment, then plunge again, disintegrating, into the night, in which I would like to melt with them too.

Oh, even had the night been more full of harmonies, the air more veiled in mist, the perfumes more laden with love, what could I retain of it all, this morning, but a fleeting

souvenir, a little ash which, lying in a hollow of my heart
for a breeze to scatter, can leave nothing behind but a
burning smart.

. . . There, farther on, in the empty road is a heap of
stones one can sit on. I shall go back to it every evening, at
sunset; I shall go alone . . . Farther on, to the right, the
dunes begin; facing me the desert. This road leads to Tolga;
and it is over there above Tolga that the sky catches fire. The
sand of the dune, glowing at first, turns to ash. At the heart
of the desert a marsh changes into a pool of blood. The oasis
stretches away darkly on my left. A mist rises from the
ground, recedes and bathes the gardens in blue. No softness
here, no melancholy; only a boundless, inhuman peace, dif-
fused glory and a splendid insensibility. Serenely, with

indifference the night ascends. Very far away some nomads light their fires.

If the days are unsettled, the nights are beautiful – more beautiful than the memory one keeps of them. How can I go indoors, or sleep, knowing that outside, in the soft air, that gleaming clarity persists, and knowing that before I leave here the moon every night will light the town just a little later for me, and every night wane just a little more.

The Springs of Oumach

The sun here whitened the reeds, laurels grew in such abundance that, making one's way through them, one forgot the desert; they overran and hid the springs, and created a retreat, almost of mystery, which one knew to be a haunt at night of hyenas. The hot springs spurted out of a subsidence in the soil; while, on more open, lower ground washerwomen came sometimes to do their washing. The sulphur waters coloured the bed of the springs green, which gave them an appearance of greater depth. The sun reared above them.

Last year some nomads set fire to the scrub; they laid waste this secret spot of the desert, according to Arab custom; in the rugged fold of the ground, the approach to which nothing conceals any more, the mystery of the spring lies exposed; and now the water surges up to the sun with no further modesty.

The washerwomen have fled. This morning we met only a few haggard nomads; beside the spring there was a dead donkey; and at night, we thought, hyena or jackal, sniffing the air fouled by the carcase, would come running up to finish tearing away the flesh.

No, I will not waste this splendid day by working! I will stay out until nightfall. Radiant weather . . . I address my prayers this morning to the Apollo of the Sahara; I see him with golden locks, black limbs and porcelain eyes. This morning my joy is perfect.

During the day's fast, while poor Bachir, my friend, waits for night to come, he strips away the tiny leaves for the kief he will smoke in the evening. Thus, sunk in the miseries of his existence, he awaits the night of the tomb, and prepares his paradise.

When I speak to him of his wretchedness:

'There's nothing to be done, Monsieur Gide, it will come to an end.' – By that he does not mean that he hopes ever to be rich, no, but that what will come to an end will be his life.

Everything else is plunged in night already; but in the West an inflammation lingers on. One can see it, deep in the desert, at the end of each street one crosses. A redness, drawn from the last fires of the sun's rays, hangs over there: and there, brushing the dune, level with the sand, runs a more crimson line, a blood-red glowing cloud, like a long scratch on the sky. Oh, with what abundant gold above the dune the vanished sun, a little time ago, flooded the plain! What mist rises from it now! Behind its delicate veil of blue the oasis little by little withdraws.

Hot Springs

What do I come to seek here again? – Perhaps, just as a body afire finds joy in diving naked into cold water, my spirit, stripped of everything, drenches in the ice-cold desert its fervour.

The pebbles on the ground are beautiful. The salt gleams. Over death floats a dream.

I took one of these pebbles in my hand; but no sooner was it off the ground than it lost its brilliance, its beauty.

Little flute with four holes, by which the tedium of the desert tells its tale, I compare you with this country, and stay to listen to you scattering your flute-notes in the night. Ah, of how few elements here are composed our sounds and our silence! The smallest change tells. – Water, sky, earth and palms . . . I am in admiration, slight instrument, of all the subtle diversity I relish in your monotony, according to the emphasis he imparts in hurrying his measure or in lulling it beneath his charming breath, the child-musician with nimble fingers.

I would wish that, from page to page, by evoking four changing tones, the sentences I write here could be for you, what for me this flute has been, what has been for me the desert – of a diverse monotony.

Droh

At the orchards' end, with no escape, the water stagnates and in a natural ditch guards on this side the oasis. It seems, long before entering, that the road lays siege to it; it delays; it seeks a devious way. It seems also as if, repelled by the delusive oasis, it hesitates. The approach to Droh, startling of aspect, is hideous. The soil under the palms is ugly, it appears spongy, as in some places was that at M'reyer, near the chott . . . Yes indeed, one hesitates to enter; the road takes another turn, overshoots, then, at last, from the side of the low mountains, profits by a sally of the oasis out of the swamps into a strangling gully of rocks. Here is the gate to the village.

Oh, I recognize it step by step. I savour again, harshly, deliciously, its horror. The same half-naked bodies stretch themselves at the feet of the same walls . . . What then! Droh had not ceased to exist! And when I shall have gone it will continue its existence! Was it necessary to return and touch all this to believe it? What need have I of this inexorable desolation and to ensure what joy? – Yes, henceforth you know that it is there, that it exists. What more is there to ask now? What do you wait for? Go back! – Not yet . . .

There is at the heart of this desolate oasis a place, confused and dark. I want to go there. There all paths are lost; the foot sinks the moment it does not tread on tufted ground;

113

but, a few steps on, the rotting soil, I know, yields up some reeds . . . Here they are! This is the hour when the sun most delicately silvers them. It is enough for a bird to light on them to bend their stalks. Out of a complex tangle of laurels they spring very high; their rods shine in the blue air.

I wanted to pick some; but no sooner in my hand than nothing remained but rough spindle, muffled at the tips in hemp-grey tufts without beauty.

. . . And in this oasis where I wander again – for I tell myself that never shall I return – on this side is some running water; it flows and sings round the foot of this palm-tree; floods a vine beside it, which twines itself round the palm's shaft; sinuously embraces it; then with a bound is level with its crest; it loses itself amongst the branches, emerges, spreads, divides, then falls back all on one side in a display of large leaves which the late autumn has gilded. The sun plays through it. No, even loaded with ripe grapes, your profusion, passionate vine, would not have seemed to me so beautiful! – or does it need the disenchantment all around to add such accent of splendour to your unexpected glow of gold . . . Another! – and another! – I had not seen them last year. – Oh, shall I be wishing to return?

Sunday

The fast ended during the night. This morning the exhausted people want to throw off their sadness; but it is raining. Today should be joyous; it is dismal. We climbed the ruins of the old fort, where prayers are held in the open air.

Thick mud sticks to one's shoes; the Arabs' piety falters; will they really kneel on the soaking ground?

Some move off towards the neighbouring mosque; we go with them. At about nine o'clock the sky lightens a little, and the prayers are announced. We climb back to the old fort. There, nearly one hundred and fifty Arabs have installed themselves as best they can on mats for their devotions. To their left, a very old priest is helped up on to a simple pulpit of earth. After some invocations which the people repeat in chorus, he starts a kind of semi-liturgical sermon, which he intones in a fine, prophetic, tired voice. Towards the end of the sermon it starts to rain again.

We were only a few people withdrawn respectfully on the right, – and even from these companions of mine I had to stand apart to hide my tears. In this vanquished people's piety, which the gloomy heavens do not seem to accept, in this despairing faith in something else, in this appeal, the desolation of the desert finds its voice and ascends.

'He is speaking sad words to them,' replies Athman to my companion's questions.

Three times the aligned crowd bows, as if beneath a wind of prayer, towards Mecca, touching the ground with their foreheads.

Opposite them and in the line of prayer, about twenty paces from the preacher, on a mound stand men- and women-tourists out to photograph, as well as a group of white Sisters, also photographers: they point their cameras, joke and parody the saint's voice. They worship a different God and feel very superior.

I dreamed that I was coming back here – after some twenty years. I passed and was no longer recognized by anyone; unknown children did not smile at me; and I dared not ask what had happened to those of the past, whom I feared to recognize in those bent men, tired out by life.

So few are the elements that create harmony, that the least change very often passes unnoticed by him whose mind recoils from analysis and who plucks his pleasure without the stem. But he is surprised, when he passes by the same places, not to taste the same delights, and not knowing to what to attribute the lessening of their charm, blames himself and thinks himself grown old. It took me long to realize how much the aromatic smoke of kief in the streets of Blida was indispensable to one's inebriation; similarly, I realize only this morning that here, into the paths of the oasis, a foreign matter has entered; under the firm clay, a pulverulent, yellow lime has appeared. The rain during these last days and the footsteps of passers-by have broken up the clay into clods, and, in places, this hideous substance emerges, slowly mixes with the clay, spoils its colour, breaks up its compactness, disintegrates and dirties it. That was why the mud in these paths, which I loved, no longer seemed to me so beautiful; the clay, after the rains, is no longer so supple under the feet; dry, it is no longer so pink, nor, when it has been penetrated by the sun, are the crackles in it so delicate.

21st December

Yesterday was an Arab holiday; it hardly stopped raining all day. The state of the streets is such that one cannot attempt to cross them; one walks, brushing the walls. On the mountain-tops the water falls in snow and lays an abstract

116

whiteness over the russet landscape. Athman splashes me with mud as he walks.

'Someone,' he says, 'paid me a fine compliment today. He said to me: "Athman, my boy, you don't know who you are; you don't know your own worth."'

How far off is the time when his vanity was satisfied with a splendiferous sash!

Monday

The sister of the Jewish inn-keeper, Babou, is being married. During three nights, according to custom, there are rejoicings. Anyone can enter the house. The first night is given up to the Ouled; the second to relatives and respectable women; the third is for anyone. I looked in on the third night out of curiosity, and even more out of idleness.

It was a very vulgar inn; the weather outside was nasty, it was cold; the first room I entered was dark; but there were no celebrations there . . .

Here we are in the private apartments. I am next to a Jew in French clothes; he is a stoutening, smiling, ignoble creature. A little farther off, with her back to the wall also, is the young, rather beautiful bride; beside her an indistinct, very ugly being, with clouded eyes, sunk in sleep or drunkenness: the husband.

A woman dances; the shrill flute of Bou-Azis makes my head reel. Everyone pretends to be enjoying himself. Athman and I, pressed by the cabaret-owner, accept glasses of green mint; not knowing where to put my drink down I swallow it; but as soon as the cabaret-owner sees my empty glass, he fills it up again; the last drinks I pour on to

117

the carpet. We go out. It is raining. Leaving Athman, leaving them all, I lose myself in the night, and let the darkness for a long time bathe me.

Tuesday

Was it, following upon my intoxication yesterday, some happy relaxation of spirit . . . I entered the orchard, as Aladdin the garden of precious stones; I walked, swaying, drunk afresh with enchantment and ecstasy, inviting the faltering, frolicking sunlight and shadow to play within me. Not a sound, not a song but from the birds. No doubt at sunrise, I thought, this garden was bathed in mist, for there lingered everywhere a hint of tenderness and dampness. The morning had been splendid to start with; but, without the least breeze blowing, the sky was soon blanketed in grey. Every object lost its sparkle, its weight and its reality. I went on walking, dreamily. It seemed to me that I was not seeing, but remembering, or rather: I went forward, not doubting that the things I saw were real, but doubting whether it was really I who was seeing them – so completely had I merged with them.

Oumach

. . . The wind rose towards evening. Our horses pulled us only with difficulty, and our tracks were immediately lost in the sand into which the wheels of the break sank. How beautiful that sand was! Lifted by the wheels, it fell back like tresses of fair hair; the wheels rolling through it rustled silkily.

118

At Sidi Okba I bought for tenpence the little five-holed flute I have here. There were several of them, made of reed, in a basket, and each one had designs on it in red. The one I bought was the smallest, with the simplest designs. I did not, so to speak, choose it; of them all this one alone pleased me; as soon as I saw it, I wanted it passionately.

It was very exactly shaped but, when I came to play on it, out of its badly pierced holes there issued only discordant notes.

Sunday

The sky is clear, but the wind is icy; I need more heat to blossom.

We gathered, on the rocky slopes, some of those minute flowers without scent, without colour and without frailty. Even the corolla is woody; it shuts to the sun. Stalkless, flat on the ground, they look like cone-shaped, wooden nails; like rock-limpets. Yes, the tap-root is immediately followed by the flower. The plant remains there, expectant, hardly distinguishable from the dry sand; then, after the smallest shower, opens and looks decayed.

The extended emptiness of the desert teaches a love of detail.

119

I have sought the shelter of a garden to write; an icy wind is blowing, and everywhere in the open air one shivers.

We have decided to leave tomorrow morning. Shall I be able to? Sometimes, quite suddenly, some crumb of voluptuousness awakes in me an after-taste so secret that at once I feel myself without the courage to tear myself away from here.

Sunday night

In the little garden, which cannot be seen from the road, and which one enters through the inn – in this little garden we sat down. Night was falling slowly over it.

In it a little water flowed, a few flowers drooped.

Two thin jujube trees on either side of us formed a frame for the quivering sky in which the dying sun bled. Here Bou-Azis joined me, and here, like the song of some twilight bird, the music rose from his pipe. It was not the muffled piping to which I had grown accustomed here; but a clear, shrill, long-drawn sound, which pierced the night and at times seemed almost mournful. Athman engaged in a dialogue with it.

To each verse he sang, the flute replied and repeated the melody with a light trill. To the tune of:

My youth is wasted in exile . . .

he sang his first song, and the second to the tune of:

I knocked at the garden-gate
The nightingale answered me: 'Come in';
The rose opened the door to me,
And I was welcomed by the jasmin.

120

The last to:

> I have fasted for more than one month
> For a single kiss of her lips.

The moon, slender still, moved through the sky, which was the colour of water; it lit very weakly Bou-Azis' handsome face; I admired his nimble fingers on the reed, which was as dark as the night.

Monday night

You will not see again, I said to myself, dipping my hands into it, you will never see again, and yet here it is, this spring, by which you come at night and sit.

Here an almost silent water flows, which my hands enter noiselessly.

I hear around me the straying voices of things . . . I recall . . . I came here one night by moonlight. Some palms in the blue brightness shadowily above the water dipped their heads . . .

No, never, never again shall I say to myself, this tranquil water – and which all the same, over there, still . . .

THE RETURN

Tunis, 28th December

We searched in vain on the hill of the Belvedere for those blue dwarf irises so suavely streaked with purple; yesterday, between Constantine and Tunis, in places they bordered the road in profusion. What a pity we could not pick any! I should have liked to try and acclimatize a tuber in my Normandy garden, as I tried with that curious bulb which I brought back from the C . . ., but which has persisted for the past two years in producing nothing but leaves.

Lake of Tunis

Polders . . . which owed their beauty to nothing but the light.

All my life the emptiest spaces have attracted me.

I arrived close by the harbour. Two Italians took me off in a boat. For a long time we floated slowly between the hulls of the large vessels. We stooped to pass under the cables. Only a light breeze blew; the water of the lake was quite shallow; in places the ground emerged. For a moment our boat ran on to the mud and a stale smell rose from the labouring oars. Stakes, in varying positions or in line, drew attention to the shallows, I suppose. They looked very much like the stakes which bounded the oyster-beds in Brittany, around Locmariaquer . . . I recalled at once those sea-green stretches, and the boat I was now in became the one in which, in times gone by, I drifted more slowly, for even longer and with much greater delight between the low-lying islands of Morbihan. It was summer; the air was hot and the sea-water was luke-warm; after the sun had set, without landing, we bathed. The sea at that spot was not very deep and the colours on its bed dappled the shell-like reflections from the sky . . .

Messina, 3rd January

Unbroken rain dulls the Calabrian coast, which recedes immeasurably and at times altogether disappears; at these moments one can see nothing more through the enormous embrasure of the window, above the stone balcony, on which the low shutter throws its green reflection – one can see nothing more than the yards of two ships . . . I don't know why I write this.

Naples

From the hotel dining-room, which is brilliantly lit and appears almost luxurious after a few glasses of Falernian wine have gone to one's head, one can hear through the curtains drawn across the open window the traditional serenade. How indecently affirmative and direct such music would seem to an Arab! All that is most vulgar, declamatory and voluptuously sentimental in the Italian soul is accentuated by the facile melody. All the same, it tickles a weak spot in me, and, be there a hint of spring in the air, I am caught by it.

Naples

Between two pianolas I read, meditate and look at the sea. Oh, how easily and naturally it comes to me to accept the flashing softness of Italian splendour. I admire my own facility in ceasing to feel myself a traveller. I ponder those 'little habits' that Nietzsche commends; those which the studious exile industriously creates for himself for days, weeks or months, which are his defences against boredom and which sustain him in his work; habits, so delightful to the assiduous mind which, as soon as it is freed from the demands of the world and the 'obligations' of society and submits to no restraints but those dictated from within, nonetheless then imposes a very severe discipline on itself, always with an eye to its work, so that the strictest rules are at the same time the best-preferred. A sort of constant alertness, of carefree elation, born of the consciousness of exile, pervades the work undertaken, and thereby the mind remains attentive, braced, open to the boldest conceptions without losing for a moment its sense of the preciousness of the hour.

I am not saying this *against* Barrès, but I certainly think it *in spite* of him.

124

Rome, from Monte Pincio, end of January

These roofs are beautiful. They are lit by the sinking sun which is hidden for a moment from my sight by a narrow cloud. It has rained; mist rises from the gulfs of the streets; from the Janiculum a haze falls. Leaning, like Polymnia, with my elbows on the balustrade in the posture that makes the passer-by exclaim: 'He is a dreamer', I am not dreaming at all; I am gazing. The flat roofs, glazed by the shower, glisten. In the damp night air the chaos of houses melts; the streets seem like rivers; the squares like lakes. And rising into the evening light, domes and campaniles . . . No, I am not dreaming. And what should I dream of? In the presence of this *reality*, why should I shut my eyes to dream?

Paris, February

It gives me no great pleasure to see the others again; and I feel that they are too well aware of it.

Why let myself go, and talk of my travels in front of T . . .? True, he understands everything I can tell him about that land . . .

But he is not a glutton for that sort of thing.

Cuverville, July

I am re-reading my travel-notes today. Publish them for whom? – They will be like those resinous secretions which refuse to yield their perfume until warmed by the hand that holds them.

Cuverville, August

I love a perfect, robust summer, and the peaceful violence of the sun. I love the noonday hour, when the shrill cries of the morning are succeeded by an overpowering heat in the plain, when the air quivers over the reaped fields and in the burning furrow the lark stretches its wings. Inhaling the smell of the ferns, I walked in the stifling wood, to the very edge of it, until nightfall.

I love the scent of the delightful evening, the shadows of the hayricks, and this sea-mist, which in our country often rises at the time the sun sets, spreads, dampens the plain and, just before night comes, brings relief by a sudden freshening of the air.

What more can you desire, exacting heart, heart that can never tire?

. . . During these hot days I think of the migrations of the nomads; oh, could one but stay here, and at the same time flee elsewhere! Oh, to be changed to air, to disintegrate, and that an azure breath, in which I had dissolved, might journey . . . !

Tonight, as soon as I had gone to my room, I heard through my open window, not far off, the shouts of the harvesters who, the harvest done, were at last returning to their village. In a cart the women and children sprawl on the hay; the men escort them on foot. They are all drunk. Their singing is no more than hoarse bellowing. Sometimes there is a louder bellow, from a conch, the only instrument they know how to play. How many times in years gone by, when I heard those shouts in the plain, ringing out for me like a rallying-cry, I ran . . . how many times! Is this really all their intoxication can yield? They are ugly people and their gods are crude. Oh, how many times, after running towards them, have I returned, disgusted, almost in tears . . .

Again tonight, these songs attract me.

End of September

The water of the oued was so warm that it was a delight to bathe in it. At the first plunge one felt that it was scarcely less burning than the air; but it had an even heat and soon grew pleasant; then, when one stepped out, the air on one's wet skin seemed cool. We would dive in again

then. Then stretch ourselves in the sun; then in the shade;
it was as refreshing as the evening air. – Oh, wide loose
garments of the Arabs! –

Companion! Companion! Comrade! In the autumn of
Normandy I dream of spring in the desert.

Palm-trees whispering in the wind! Almond-trees rustling
with bees! Warm winds! Sugar-sweet air! . . .

A squall out of the North beats against my window. It has
been raining for three days. – Oh, how beautiful the caravans were, at Touggourt, when at dusk the sun sank into
the salt.

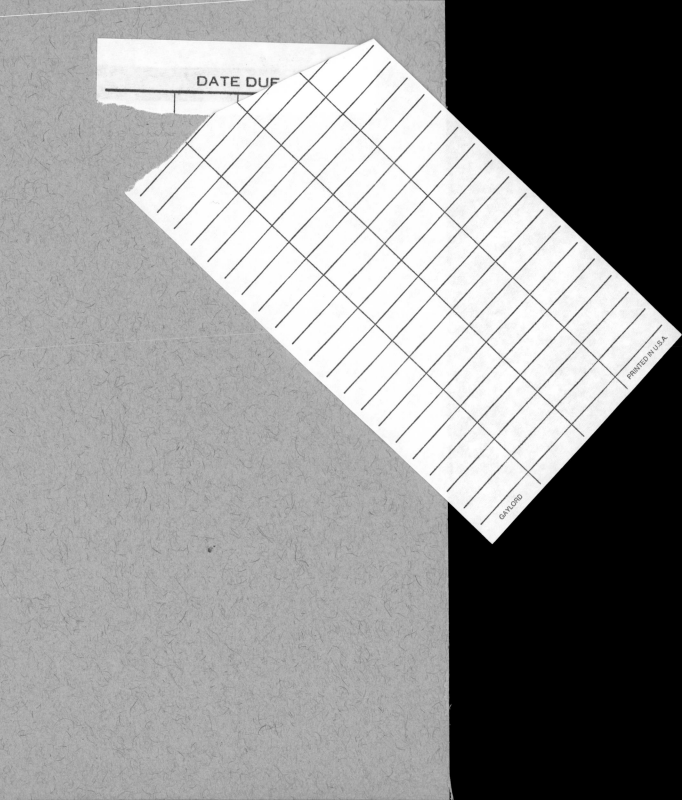

DATE DUE

GAYLORD

PRINTED IN U.S.A.